SARA, BOOK 3

A Talking Owl
is Worth A Thousand Words!

*A remarkable new way of looking
at some old ways of having fun...
An exciting adventure in joy.*

Books By Abraham-Hicks:

A New Beginning I — 1988
Handbook for Joyous Survival

A New Beginning II — 1991
A Personal Handbook to Enhance Your
Life, Liberty and Pursuit of Happiness

Sara, Book 1
*The Foreverness
of Friends of A Feather* — 1995
An inspired narrative of a child's
experiential journey into the knowingness
that All Is Well. (It really is.)

The Science of Deliberate Creation
Daily Planning Calendar/Workbook — 1996
A 365 Day Course in Spiritual Practicality

Sara, Book 2
*Sara & Seth, Solomon's
Fine Featherless Friends* — 1999
A fresh, fast paced, fun-filled adventure in wisdom...
A giant step in your journey of becoming.

Sara, Book 3
*A Talking Owl
Is Worth A Thousand Words* — 2002
A remarkable new way of looking
at some old ways of having fun...
An exciting adventure in joy.

*If your favorite local bookstore doesn't carry these books,
they may be ordered directly or online from www.abraham-hicks.com*

SARA, BOOK 3

A Talking Owl
is Worth A Thousand Words!

By Esther and Jerry Hicks

Illustrations by Caroline Garrett

For information:
Jerry and Esther Hicks
P.O. Box 690070
San Antonio, TX 78269
(830) 755-2299

Printed in the U.S.A.
First edition, June, 2002

Hicks, Esther and Jerry
Sara, Book 3:
A Talking Owl is Worth a Thousand Words
ISBN: 0-9621219-9-1

Abraham-Hicks Publications
www.abraham-hicks.com

FOREWORD

As we drove, today, through the unbelievably beautiful backroads of Illinois, and Indiana, Jerry read to me this just completed third Sara book: *A Talking Owl Is Worth A Thousand Words.* (What a pleasure it was for me to hear it, for the first time, in this way.) We parked the motor coach, and checked into our seminar hotel, and I sat back in a comfortable overstuffed chair, eyes closed, feet up, basking in the fulfilling feeling of having completed another book—when, almost instantly, my mind began filling with powerful words, flowing for the next Sara book.

So, we're off again!

I hope you are enjoying this Sara series as much as I am. Sara and Seth and Annette, and Solomon are as real to me as anyone I know, and I, too, am loving what I am learning as I watch their lives unfold.

With love,
Esther

INTRODUCTION

Within all that is, and isn't; including every place, and non place; swirling through the Unlimited Universal Environment, await the answers to everything you have ever needed to know about anything. And from where Sara's teacher, Solomon, exists, in that Universal Environment, comes to you this *Sara, Book 3.*

You are about to embark upon a remarkable and exciting experience—an adventure into a new way of seeing things; a new way of looking at some old ways of having fun.

And so, expect to experience some new perceptions. Expect to reconnect with your invulnerable Self. Expect to learn how to experience adventure without fearing risk.

Learn how: It all turns out right, anyway; you never get it done, and you can't get it wrong; you can feel good under all conditions; you can call it good or bad, but it's all good; every "accident" has a cause; you can find the wanted masked by the unwanted; you can go from jealousy and guilt to feeling good; you can perceive death and still feel good; there is no death; your body naturally heals; you can attract harmonious relationships; you were meant to be happy; you can have everything you want...

We are all in this together. We have, somehow, been attracted to each other, in this moment, as a result of the intentions and resulting vibrations of each of us. For example: for over a decade, Esther and I have traveled to as many as 60 cities a year, opening our Workshops to thousands of persons to ask any questions they wanted to ask—and from those thousands of questions have evolved the series of delicious *Sara* books. And as this *Sara, Book 3* is distributed to thousands of readers, more questions will be evoked... For instance: a teacher in a San Francisco public school (his students call his classroom, Bergland) used the first *Sara* book, last year, as a class text book, and he suggested that the students (about 30 sixth graders) email, to us, their personal questions and their suggestions as to what they would like to see happen in the next *Sara* books. (Although we have too many other commitments, these days, to respond like that again—we created, and gave to each of them, for their graduation, a booklet with each of their excellent questions, and Solomon's answers. A great time was had by all!) The uncanny part of the story was: Although, none of them had read any part of the *Sara, Book 3* outline—nearly every suggestion of what they wanted to happen next, was already written in the manuscript! Never before have I been so aware of just how closely we are spiritually intertwined and how our questions are being answered, often before we are aware that we are asking.

So, here we are, you with your asking, and this book with the answers. What a perfect point of cocreation! This material has been created to add to your level of joy, no matter how happy you already are, and it has been created for you, if you so desire, to share with, or teach to, or give to others who may not, yet, be as happy as you.

We are living in a time when there is more opportunity for happiness than ever before in our recorded history. And yet, among the billions of us here, there remain some relatively small clusters of persons who seem to consciously band together and deny themselves that readily available opportunity for "earthy pleasure". For the majority of us, who were neither born nor coerced into one of those more stringent systems of beliefs, we can somewhat understand, if not readily accept, their "choices of earthly pain". However, once we begin to hear that "we are each free to choose, and that by our choices, we create our own experience," we find it more difficult to understand why there is so much fear, illness, pain... and general unhappiness, being experienced in our civilized environment. In other words, why should there be any pain or suffering in this era of so much opportunity for freedom, growth and joy?

Solomon, Sara's ethereal friend, teaches that experiencing anything less than Well-being is unnatural, and so this book is simply about discovering how to return to your naturally happy self—no matter what! This is a book about allowing it, and then being the example of it—and then about sharing your Well-being with others.

The following passage is an excerpt of Solomon's words to Sara; words that summarize the simplicity and clarity of this thrilling adventure into the discovery of how joyous and fulfilling our lives are meant to be:

Sara, what about making your happiness your main issue?
"Nothing is more important than that you feel good."

People often believe that things have to be a certain way before they can feel good. And then, when they discover that they don't have the power or the votes, or the strength to make things be the way they want—they resign themselves to powerless, unhappy lives.

Understand that your power lies in your ability to see things in a way that keeps you feeling good, and when you are able to do that—you have the power to achieve anything that you desire.

Everything that you desire is trying to make its way to you, but you must find the way to let it in—and only in feeling good, can you let in those things you desire.

You live in a big world, Sara, with many other people who may want things to be different than you want them to be. You cannot convince or coerce them all to agree with you; you cannot destroy all of them who do not agree with you. Your only path to a joyous, powerful life experience is to decide, once and for all, that no matter what—you intend to feel good. And as you practice turning your thoughts to things that do feel good—now you have discovered the secret to life...

Esther and I have found much pleasure in discovering the depth of Solomon's "Secret to Life" as it unfolds, page by page, through this third book of the Sara series. And we are imagining the fun you will have as you, too, discover the treasures contained between the pages of this delightfully powerful book.

The purpose of life is joy; its basis is freedom; its result is growth. Sara and her friend, Solomon, are about to add another chapter to the fulfillment of your purpose in life.

And so, off we go, on anther adventure... an adventure in joy.

From my heart,

CHAPTER ONE

Apleasant smile washed over Sara's face as she thought about getting together with Seth, her best friend in the whole world, to catch up on what had been happening over the last few weeks of summer. She gazed up at the clear blue sky and breathed in, deeply, the fresh mountain air—and felt glad for her life.

"I am so happy school is starting," Sara said, out loud, to herself. But, it wasn't school starting that Sara was glad for; it was having more time to be with her friend, Seth.

Seth lived over on Thacker's Trail, not far from where Sara lived with her mother and father and her little brother, Jason. Sara and Seth had discovered so many things in common, like their love for the outdoors, and their love for animals, and their mutual appreciation for learning new things. But at home their lives were very different. Not so much in outward appearances, for, after all, they did live in the same neighborhood. It was just that Sara seemed to have the freedom to do pretty much as she pleased, but Seth's parents seemed to allow him far less freedom; his list of chores and family responsibilities was a very long one, and Sara found it difficult to believe that there was really that much that needed to be tended to at Seth's house. She had decided, very soon after coming to know him that the majority of Seth's chores were more about keeping him busy than about doing things that really needed to be done. But, Seth never complained. He always treated his parents with respect and always did as he was told. And there was something about that, that Sara liked very much.

But, once school started, Seth's parents seemed to loosen their tight rein on him, and he was able to find some time, nearly every day after school, to play with Sara. And so, Sara oozed happy anticipation as she half-ran, half-walked down the country road toward the school grounds.

Sara stepped off to the side of the road as she heard the engine of a truck coming from behind, and once it passed, she reclaimed her place walking right down the middle of the country road. She came to the corner where Seth's street intersected with hers, and she looked down the road toward Thacker's Trail and toward Seth's house. "Come on, Seth, where are you?" Sara said, anxiously. She could barely wait to see him and talk to him.

She stopped for a while, dropping her new and, for today only, empty, book bag to her feet and waited. "Seth, where are you?"

Sara saw a big dump truck coming from the direction of Seth's house, and a big cloud of dust engulfed her as it passed. She squinted her eyes and waved her hand in front of her face to try to clear the air. Still, there was no sign of Seth.

"Oh, well, I'll catch up with him at school," she consoled herself, picking up her bag and walking backwards, hoping that one last look would find him running down the road toward her; but no Seth.

Sara's walk to school was not terribly long, and the time usually passed quickly as she pondered her own happy thoughts while she walked. Anyone observing Sara, these days, would tell you that it is obvious that she is a truly happy girl. And those same people would also tell you that it has not always been that way, and that an amazing transformation had taken place. But, of all of the people in Sara's life, only one of them knows the secrets behind her amazing transformation—and that person is Seth.

"Good morning, Sara!" Sara heard Mr. Matson call to her as she passed the service station that he had owned and operated even before she was born.

"Hi, Mr. Matson," Sara called back, smiling, as she watched him carefully wiping every single bug from Mrs. Pittsfield's windshield. Sara liked Mr. Matson. They nearly always exchanged brief and happy words whenever Sara walked past his service station. Mr. Matson had seen Sara's amazing transformation, too, but had no idea what was behind it.

Sara stopped on the Main Street bridge and peered at the rapidly moving water below. She took a deep breath and looked up into the trees, and smiled. How she did love this place. She had always loved this old bridge and the wonderful river that flowed beneath it, and the lovely old trees that towered above it. In fact, it was on this very spot that she had first seen Seth. It seemed fitting that she would first lay eyes on her best friend in the whole world while being in her favorite spot in the whole world.

Sara could not understand why more people had not taken a liking to her favorite spot, but, at the same time, it pleased her that she always had it to herself. Sara walked along, thinking about this wonderful place, and smiled. *So many things are like that,* she thought, *you can't really tell what they are like from the outside. You have to get inside of them to know what they are really about.*

Many years earlier, a large truck had lost control, while trying to avoid running over a wandering dog, and had slammed into the metal railing that lined the Main Street bridge. Once the truck was pulled to safety, the old railing was never the same again. No repair was ever attempted, but instead, it was left, as the truck had left it, bent way out over the river. Most people complained that it was an eyesore, while others didn't think that the railing had ever been particularly attractive, and apparently no one thought it was worth spending the money to repair it, so nothing was ever done to straighten the railing back up again.

One day, while walking home from school, Sara noticed that the poles were still securely fastened to the bridge and that the mesh wire, stretched between the poles, hung like a cradle right out over the water. At first, it was a little scary to see and hear the fast moving river surging down below, but soon, Sara felt certain that the railing would hold her, and very quickly it had become her favorite place to be. She would lay right out over the river, like being cradled in a giant spider web, looking down, watching things floating by. Sara didn't know why, but she felt better here, dangling out over the river, than any place she had ever been.

So, there she had been, happily dangling there, one warm afternoon, when Seth's family drove into Sara's town. Sara had hardly noticed the sputtering old truck, overloaded with everything that Seth's family owned. Her only clear recollection, of that moment in time, was locking eyes with Seth, a new, intense boy, who appeared to be about her same age, riding in the back of the truck.

Today, as Sara walked along, enjoying the crunching leaves beneath her feet, and remembering the momentous meeting of her best friend, ever—a shiver of pleasure rippled up her spine. So much had happened in the short time Sara had known Seth, that their first meeting seemed like lifetimes ago. She smiled as she walked, feeling glad for their friendship.

Although Sara had felt an instant attraction to this new boy, she had been determined that she was not going to let him get into the middle of her life and mess things up. And so, when Sara discovered that Seth's family was moving into the old Thacker House, she had felt enormous distress. She didn't want anyone living there so close to her beloved Thacker's Trail.

No one in Sara's little mountain town was particularly interested in Thacker's Trail; no one except Sara. But that is because no one in Sara's town knew what Sara knew about

Thacker's Trail. Sara thought it was strange that people could live all around there, so close to something so wonderful and amazing, and not even know about it. But that was just fine by Sara. She liked it that no one else knew what she knew about Thacker's Trail. And she had intended to keep it just that way.

"Hmm," Sara said, softly, under her breath. Those thoughts and feelings about Seth now felt so distant. They came from very far in the past. Because, now, Seth was as much a part of her life and the incredible meaning of Thacker's Trail as was Sara, and she liked it that only Seth shared her secrets.

For many years, before Seth had moved into her town, Sara had spent her summer months, and countless hours after school, exploring the paths, and climbing the trees, in the wooded area that surrounded Thacker's Trail. There was nothing that Sara loved more than to duck off of the road, and sneak down the trail into the woods, to spend a happy hour, or so, in the seclusion of one of her temporary huts or forts that she had made from whatever she could gather from the woods. They were never very substantial; the next rain or windstorm usually caused them to fall apart, but they were fun while they lasted.

Sara had not known that Seth had felt the same way that she did about having a secret place to spend time, and she had not been aware that he had been sneaking into the woods, for many weeks, constructing an amazing tree house high up in the cottonwood trees, overlooking the creek. Sara had never, before, felt as excited as she had felt on the day Seth unveiled his incredible tree house to her, and announced that it would be their "secret place". It was almost too good to stand.

Sara remembered the day Seth took her to the tree house for the first time. He had said he had something amazing, that she just had to see, over on Thacker's Trail, and it had made her heart jump right into her mouth, because she was afraid that Seth had discovered her precious secret. She remembered how eagerly he had guided her through the woods, turning down one trail and then another, leading her deep into the woods, and right to the edge of the river. And she remembered her great relief in realizing that Seth had not uncovered her secret at all, but, instead, he had spent hundreds of hours constructing an incredible tree house, high up in the old cottonwood trees, overlooking the river.

Sara's first impression of Seth's tree house was still vivid in her mind: She could barely believe her eyes. There were perfectly placed boards, nailed on the backside of the tree, forming a ladder, leading up, up, up into this giant of a tree. And extending out from the tree house, was a platform. "A launching pad," Seth had called it, for swinging out over the river.

And now, all this time later, Sara still remembered, vividly, the wild excitement she had felt when she first saw Seth's launching pad: A big rope that was tied way up on a high branch, which allowed them to jump from the tree house and swing way out over the river, which they did, almost every day after school, weather permitting, and sometimes even not permitting.

Sara and Seth had spent many blissful hours swinging on this great rope from this amazing tree house high in the trees. And it was there, in their secret hideaway, that Sara had finally entrusted, to Seth, the precious secrets of Thacker's Trail.

CHAPTER TWO

"Sara, do you want to come on in?" Sara was startled to see Mr. Marchant, the school principal, holding the front door open for her. She had been so deep in her own thoughts she hadn't even realized that she was on the school grounds.

"Oh, yes," Sara mumbled, trying to focus back into the moment. "Thanks."

The corridors were full of students greeting each other and busily moving about. Sara stood back against the wall and searched through the crowd, looking for Seth. "Hey, Sara," she heard, again and again, as other students, she hadn't seen throughout the summer, greeted her.

All day long, as she moved from class to class, Sara watched for Seth. She wanted so much to see him. It seemed like forever since they had talked.

And then, Sara saw Seth making his way through the crowd in the hallway. She walked faster, trying to catch up with him, but as she got closer, she could see that he was with someone Sara did not know. She watched the two of them walking and talking, and laughing. *Who is that?* Sara wondered.

It was very unusual that Sara would not recognize someone. For the most part, the same group of students had been with Sara from the day she entered the school system in this small mountain town, and when someone new did move in, everyone learned who they were, right away. Everyone knew everyone.

Sara walked slowly, not wanting to catch up with them. She saw them stop in the hallway, seeming to be having a very interesting conversation about something. Then the girl laughed again, and walked away from Seth.

Sara felt a knot in her stomach. She ducked into the girls' bathroom. She gazed blankly into the mirror while cool water ran through her fingers. She patted her face with her cool hands and wiped her face on a paper towel. "What is wrong with me?" she chastised herself. The bell rang, letting Sara know she was almost late for her class, and so she grabbed her book bag and hurried to her classroom.

After a long afternoon of struggling to focus on what was happening in her classroom, Sara dragged herself down the path toward the tree house. She felt terrible. In fact, she felt so bad, she considered not going there at all. The tree house was such a happy, good-feeling place; it did not seem like a match, in any way, to the way Sara was feeling right now, but the idea of staying away felt even worse. "What is wrong with me?" she scolded herself.

Sara rounded the last bend in the trail and came into view of the tree house. *I hope he's already here,* Sara thought. But all was quiet. Seth was not there. So she dropped her book bag at the base of the tree, climbed the ladder, and sat on the platform, and waited.

Seth came blasting through the bushes. "Sara, are you up there?" he called, as he climbed the ladder.

"Yes, Hi," Sara called back, trying to cover up the way she was feeling, with a cheerful sound.

Seth climbed up and sat awkwardly on the bench beside Sara.

"So, what's up?" Sara began.

"Not much. How about with you?" Seth answered.

"So, did you have a good day?" Sara did not know what she wanted to hear from Seth. All she knew was that she wanted to feel better, and she hoped that he might say something to her that would help her to feel better.

"Yeah, I had a good day. Did you?"

"Yeah, okay, I guess."

It didn't look like Seth was going to volunteer anything, so Sara decided that she would have to be more direct.

"So, anything new happen since the last time we talked?"

"No, not really." Seth nervously untied his shoelace and tightened it and tied it again. "Well, wanna swing on the rope?" Seth said, standing up and looking out across the river. He did not look at Sara.

"No, I don't really feel like it. You go ahead." Sara said, limply.

"Nah, I guess I better get goin'. I'll see ya tomorrow."

Seth climbed down the ladder.

Sara sat, dumbfounded. This is not the way this day was supposed to happen. This was supposed to be a happy day of catching up with each other and getting back in the swing of swinging from the rope. Sara had been so looking forward to this day. What in the world was going on?

Sara watched Seth disappear into the trees. She could barely remember ever feeling so bad.

CHAPTER THREE

The next morning, Sara awakened with a happy heart. She stretched a nice long stretch, and sat up in her bed. But then she remembered Seth and the new girl at school, and that tense uncomfortable feeling washed right back over her. She flopped back onto the bed and pulled the covers around her. She was not ready to get up to face this day. What she really wanted to do was to fall back asleep, away from this awful feeling.

Her mother knocked on her door, opening it and walking in at the same time. "Sara, are you up? It's nearly 7:30!"

Why bother knocking if you are going to just walk right in, anyway? Sara thought. She felt extremely irritable. She didn't want to get up—ever!

"I know, I know," Sara grumbled. "I'm coming."

"Everything all right, Honey?" her mother asked. She hadn't seen Sara in a bad mood for a very long time. It was actually shocking to see this positive, sweet girl in such a terrible mood the first thing in the morning.

"Everything is just dandy," Sara quipped back, sarcastically.

Her mother felt the sting of Sara's response, but decided not to reply and make it more. She quietly closed the door.

Sara sat on the edge of her bed feeling even worse because of her unpleasant response to her mother. "Geeze, what's wrong with me?" she whined, flopping back on her bed, and pulling the covers up around her, again.

"I'll see you tonight," Sara heard her mother call out, "Your lunch is on the table." Sara heard the back door close, and the squeaky garage door open. She heard the tires of her mother's car crunching through the gravel driveway. Tears welled up in Sara's eyes. *I'm such a bad daughter,* she thought. *What is the matter with me?*

Well, if I don't get going, I'm going to be late for school. Sara quickly dressed, grabbed the paper bag, containing her lunch, and hurried out the door. She looked at her watch. "Ten minutes 'til the first bell. Well, if I run, I can make it," she said, breaking into a gentle run. Her book bag swung back and forth in a gentle rhythm, and as she ran — Sara's gloom lifted.

As she came through the front gates, she heard the first school bell ring, and she broke into a broad smile. "Good job!" she complimented herself. *Nothing like a little triumph over crisis to cheer one up,* she thought.

CHAPTER FOUR

"Sara, wait up!" Sara heard Seth calling from behind. She looked back over her shoulder as Seth ran to catch up with her.

"I've got something I want to talk with you about."

Sara didn't like the way that made her stomach feel.

"What?" Sara tried to sound calm and normal.

"Hey, isn't this a great day?" Seth stalled.

Sara could feel Seth's uneasiness. It was as if he knew that she didn't want to hear what he had to say. Sara had a pretty good idea what it was he wanted to talk about, and Seth was right; she didn't want to hear it. She braced herself for his next words. She deliberately remained quiet. She had no intention of making this one bit easier for him.

"Umm, I wanted to... well, you know how we... well, there's this girl..."

There it was. Sara was certain, now, that she didn't want Seth to go any further.

"A.... well..."

Sara didn't say a word. She walked along, holding her book bag in her arms in front of her, resting her chin on the bag while she looked down at the path.

Seth stammered on, a bit more, and then just blurted. "Sara, I want to show Annette our tree house."

Well, there it was, right out in the open. Seth had a new friend. And obviously she was a special friend, because Seth and Sara had promised each other that they would never ever tell anyone else about the tree house.

Sara's heart was pounding and her mouth felt very dry. She tried to swallow. She didn't want her words to come out sounding as strange as she felt.

"How come?"

Seth slowed his pace. He hadn't expected such a direct question from Sara. He had anticipated that she would ask, "Who is Annette?" and he then he would explain that she is a new girl in his class who sits across the aisle from him. But Sara's question required a careful response. Seth knew that the truthful answers to her question would not set well with Sara. "Why do I want to show Annette our tree house? Because she is a great girl, full of life and fun, who would appreciate the tree house as much as we do." Seth didn't think that was the best thing to say to Sara. He would never lie to Sara. But he also did not want to upset her. What a terrible dilemma. How could he be truthful with Sara, and not upset her, and still get something that was very important to him? Then it came to him. He felt ease wash over him, and he said: "Because I remember how hard it was to be the new kid in town, and then meeting you, Sara, made all the difference in the world to me. I just thought that you could help Annette feel better about being here, like you made me feel better about being here."

Seth was so intense and so sincere. Sara felt relief wash over her, and she looked up for the first time.

"Oh, well, then, I guess...."

"Okay, then, we'll meet you by the flag pole after school tomorrow." Seth ran up the steps of the building, and then turned around and called back to Sara. "I can't go there tonight. There's something I have to do. Tomorrow, we'll see you there tomorrow."

Sara watched Seth scampering away from her—and then the full impact of what had just happened hit her.

"Seth, wait, what about..."

Seth bounded into the building and the big door banged shut behind him.

"Oh, man." Sara whined to herself. "What is Seth thinking? What about Solomon?"

For the rest of the afternoon, Sara could barely focus on anything that was happening in class. All she could think about was Seth and the tree house, and this new girl, what was her name? Annette? And what in the world would they do about Solomon?

Did Seth forget that the tree house was usually where he and Sara, and Solomon met? Of course he didn't. How could he forget something like that? So, if Seth wants to show the tree house to Annette, does that mean that he wants to share Solomon, too?

Sara's teacher turned out the lights and started the projector. Light shot from the projector and images danced on the screen at the front of the classroom. Sara leaned her head against the wall, sighed a deep sigh, and closed her eyes. What was she to do?

She thought about how, as she got to know Seth, it began to feel logical to share her secret with him, but she still remembered how risky it felt, not only because he might not like her once he found out about Solomon, but she worried that he might ruin everything for her.

How in the world do you go about explaining to someone, that you talk, on a regular basis, with a talking owl, named Solomon, who knows everything about you and everything about everything else, too? Sara was certain that, for much less, they lock people up, and throw away the key. And so, she had felt overwhelming relief when Seth didn't even flinch as she had revealed, to him, her strange relationship with Solomon.

Sara tried to imagine Annette's response to it all: "Oh, hi, Annette. Welcome to our tree house. And, by the way, one day I was walking through the woods where I met a big owl sitting on a fence post, and the owl said to me, 'Hello, Sara, isn't this a lovely day?' And I said, 'Oh, yes, isn't it?' And then my rotten little brother and his horrible little friend shot my owl friend, but that was okay, because he came back to life again, with feathers and everything, and isn't it your turn to swing on the rope?"

Most people are not ready to hear that you have a talking owl for a friend, who knows everything about everything! You just don't talk about things like this with just anybody. What could Seth be thinking? Why would he take a chance on telling someone else about Solomon, and spoiling everything?

Feeling exhausted, Sara put her head down on her desk and fell asleep. Immediately, she found herself inside a dream, sitting in the top of the tree house, alone, with Solomon.

"Solomon, what in the world is Seth thinking? Why isn't he keeping our promise?"

Well, Sara, I suspect that he is thinking how happy he is that you shared your secret with him.

"But Solomon..."

The teacher turned the lights back on in the classroom, jolting Sara from her nap and from her conversation with Solomon. As she opened her eyes, she heard Solomon's voice in her head; *We are birds of a feather, Sara. All is well, here.*

CHAPTER FIVE

Feeling worried and uncomfortable, Sara made her way to the tree house. She didn't know what Seth had to do that was so important that he couldn't come to the tree house, today, but she was glad he wasn't coming. Right now, Sara wanted to talk to Solomon. Seth seemed determined to open their circle to include Annette, and now Sara knew that Solomon was in agreement, too. *I liked things the way they were.* Sara pouted. *Why does everything have to be changing all the time, anyway? After tomorrow nothing will be the same.*

Sara climbed the ladder and flopped down on the floor of the tree house, and looked up into the tree. As usual, Solomon was sitting on a branch, high up in the tree. He waited for Sara to climb the ladder and make herself comfortable, and then, as he had done hundreds of times, before, he glided down beside her.

Well, hello, Sara, isn't this a wonderful day?

Sara looked at Solomon, but she didn't speak. She did not think this was a wonderful day. And she knew that he knew that she did not think that this was a wonderful day. She also knew that Solomon would never see any day as less than wonderful, which only served to point out, even more clearly to Sara, that Solomon was, in this moment, on a very different vibrational wavelength than she was.

Look at the glorious sky, Sara. Have you ever seen such a beautiful sky?

Sara had not noticed the sky this afternoon. Not even once. She looked off into the distance; a heavy bank of clouds was shading her from the afternoon sun, and a beautiful rainbow of pinks and purples, and blues, was clearly visible from her tree house view.

"That is especially pretty," she said, softly, feeling slightly better as she spoke.

I don't believe I've ever seen the sky look quite that way before, Solomon said.

Sara agreed. It was different than she had noticed before, also.

I guess I'd have to call that a perfect sunset, Sara. For I've never seen one I liked more. How about you?

"Yep, I guess I'd have to agree with you, Solomon." It felt odd to Sara that Solomon was now so intensely interested in the sky, when she had such a terrible knot in her stomach. *Seems like he should be helping me with my problem,* she thought.

I marvel at how perfectly lovely this sky can be, and yet how it is never the same. It is always changing. Have you noticed that, Sara?

"Yeah, I guess."

Day after day, I sit in this tree, taking in the beauty of this place, and I am amazed at the extraordinary variety of light patterns and breezes, and combinations of sun and clouds, and blue sky, that passes before me. And in all of the days I've been sitting here, not once have I seen a repeat of anything that I have seen before. The variety is remarkable.

Sara listened. She knew Solomon was making an important point with her.

Yep, perfect in this moment, and ever changing. I find that extremely fascinating. Well, Sara, I think I'll go enjoy this perfect day from a higher perspective. Have a wonderful evening, Sweet Girl.

Solomon lifted, with his powerful wings, up into the sky. Sara watched as he made a large circle and then flew off into the direction of the sunset. The sun was shining so brightly from behind the heavy clouds, they appeared to have a shining silver ring around them. Sara watched until Solomon was out of her view.

"Okay, okay, I get it. Change is a good thing." Sara said, softly. "But I don't have to like it."

CHAPTER SIX

Sara waited by the school's flagpole for Seth and Annette. She anxiously scanned the faces of person after person, trying to remember what Annette looked like. She had not really gotten a good look at her, yet, but she remembered that she was rather tall, taller than Sara, and very slender. Her hair was about the same color as Sara's, but longer and straighter.

"Sara? I'm Annette. Seth has told me so much about you."

Sara looked at the very pretty girl standing before her.

"Hi," Sara said, self-consciously running her fingers through her own long curly hair.

"Seth said you are the best friend that he has ever had and that there was no one in this town, or anywhere on the planet, for that matter, that would be better for me to know."

Sara smiled. That all sounded pretty good.

"He's so sweet, Sara. Couldn't you just eat him up?"

Sara felt that knot in her stomach.

"Yeah, I guess." Sara flushed.

Sara heard the big door on the school building bang shut. She turned around to see Seth bounding down the steps, taking two at a time. *He's sure excited about all of this,* Sara thought.

"Hey, I see you two have already met. Ready to go?"

"I am," Annette quipped, cheerfully. "I just can't wait to see whatever this amazing surprise is that you have to show me."

Yeah, yeah, yeah, Sara thought. *It's amazing, you're amazing, I'm amazing. We're all pretty darn amazing.*

Seth started out ahead of them. The sidewalk was not quite wide enough for them to walk three abreast, so Seth walked out ahead and Sara and Annette followed, side by side. *Already, I don't like this,* Sara thought to herself.

"You two, go ahead," Seth said, stepping off into the grass to let them pass. "I'll follow you."

Annette smiled. "You are such a gentleman, Seth Morris."

Yeah, yeah, yeah, Sara thought, sarcastically.

"So, Sara, Seth told me that you have lived in this town all of your life."

"Yip," Sara said, almost rudely.

Seth looked at Sara. He was surprised at her shortness with their new friend. Sara was not herself. Not even close.

Sara felt embarrassment wash over her. *What is the matter with me?* She chastised herself. *I've got no good reason to be mean to Annette. I'm sure she is a very nice person who doesn't deserve this.* She took a deep breath, swallowed, and then said, "Yip, I've always lived here. It's a good place to live, I guess. How do you like it, so far?"

"Well, it's okay. It's not like home, or what used to be home. But I guess I'll get used to it."

Annette looked sad. She didn't seem to be focused in this moment, anymore. Her eyes had a sort of distant look in them, like she was thinking of another place, far away. Sara felt sad for her. It must be hard to leave everything that is familiar, and plunge into a new place with all new people. For a moment, Sara realized what it was that Seth must have felt that made him to want to tell Annette about the tree house. *If I had met her, first, I probably would have wanted to tell her about it, too,* Sara tried to console herself.

"I've always lived in a big city," Annette continued. "But my dad says that's no place for us kids to grow up. I don't know what's so bad about growing up in a big city. Big cities have great stores and grand museums, and wonderful restaurants. Where do you guys eat around here, anyway?"

Seth and Sara looked at each other. What an odd question. "We eat at home," Sara said. "Well, mostly. Sometimes we grab a hamburger at Pete's Drugstore, and there's school lunch if you're brave enough."

"Oh," Annette sounded very disappointed.

"Well, we're almost there," Seth interrupted. "We don't have any grand museums or great restaurants here, but I'll bet we've got something you haven't seen before. But you have to promise not to tell anyone about it. It's, like, our secret, you know. Just the three of us."

Sara flinched. *Just the three of us.* That was going to take some getting used to.

Annette smiled, brightly. "What is it? I can't wait. Tell me!"

"Can't tell you. We have to show you. It's not far."

Seth moved out ahead of them and ducked off the pavement onto the dirt path. They walked along single file. Sara could not help but notice the extra lilt to his walk. *Don't get your hopes up,* Sara thought. *Annette is a city girl.*

"Tah, Dah!" Seth said, loudly, gesturing toward the tree. "Here it is. What do you think?"

"I think you are way too excited about showing me a tree; that's what I think. We do have trees in the city, you know," Annette kidded.

"Ah, not a tree like this one, ya don't," Seth said, leading Annette around to the backside.

Annette's mouth dropped open as she gazed up into this giant of a tree.

Seth grinned. He had not felt this proud of his handiwork since he had showed it to Sara, for the first time, many, many months ago.

"Seth, you made this ladder?" Annette exclaimed, standing back, trying to get a clearer view of the row of boards Seth had nailed from the base of the tree all the way up into the branches, and out of view.

"Feel like going up?"

"Wow," Annette gasped. "Do I ever!"

Oh, this is just great. She loves it, Sara thought.

Seth climbed quickly up the ladder towards the platform, and Annette followed, just as fast, right behind him. Sara slowly dragged herself up behind them.

Seth pointed out to Annette all the special features of his wonderful creation. And with an enthusiasm Sara couldn't remember ever seeing from Seth, he showed Annette the ladder that he had nailed up the backside of the big old tree; he explained how he had carefully sanded every piece so you wouldn't get slivers; he demonstrated the bucket and pulley system he had rigged, and explained how it is much easier

31

to use than trying to climb up the ladder with your arms full of things... Sara listened, wanting to feel appreciation for all of these wonderful things that Seth had built, but she didn't feel happy or proud like she had felt when he had shown them to her for the first time. She felt bad. *I thought he did these things for us, for me,* she thought.

"And that," Seth said, pointing, dramatically, "is the launching pad!"

"Launching pad? You mean...." Annette could hardly believe what she saw.

"That's how we fly through the air, with the greatest of ease!"

"All right!" Annette's voice echoed down the river.

"Sara, you want to go first, to show Annette how it's done?"

Sara jumped a little. Seth was so excited about his new friend, he had hardly spoken to Sara. She was beginning to feel like she was invisible. "No, you go first." Sara said, trying to sound cheerful.

"Okay. Here I go. Here's what you do: You put your foot in this loop. Grab hold of one of these knots. This one will probably work best for you," Seth said, showing Annette the knot he had tied for himself. "Just step off, and away you go!" Seth leaped off the platform and flew out across the river.

"Whoa!" Annette exclaimed, as Seth yahooed across the river. "This is fantastic. Oh, wow, I do love this! Hey, it's really high up here. How'd you guys find this place? I love it! I love it! I love it!"

Seth did his best dismount ever, which did not surprise Sara, and then called up to Annette. "Okay, your turn!"

Sara sat back, watching, thinking about her first swing on the rope and how awkward and scary it had felt. She remembered the first brutal dismounts that both she and Seth had experienced, tumbling into the muddy water, again and again, and she smiled inwardly, as she imagined Annette's first dismount.

Seth climbed the tree and pulled the big rope back up to the launching pad, but as he began to explain again to Annette just how to proceed, she grabbed the rope and leaped off the platform, wrapping her legs around the rope as she swung out across the river. She swung back and forth with her long pretty hair flowing out behind her. But then, Annette let go of the rope with her hands!

"Watch out!" Sara screamed.

But, Annette had wrapped her legs tightly into the rope, and she soared gracefully, upside-down, with her arms stretched out before her, as if she were flying. Back and forth she flew, laughing and squealing with each pass.

Sara looked at Seth, in amazement.

"She's a gymnast," Seth said, quietly. "Isn't she great?"

"Oh, yeah," Sara said under her breath. "Great."

Sara looked up and spied Solomon perched on a tree branch high above their heads. Solomon winked at Sara as if to reassure her that he wasn't going to hop down on the platform and start talking.

All is well, Sara, Sara heard Solomon's clear, calm voice in her head. *In time, if it is your desire, you may introduce Annette to me. Like you, and like Seth, Annette will enjoy our interaction. She is like us, Sara. She is a bird of our feather.*

"Oh, that's just great," Sara said, right out loud.

"What's great?" Annette asked.

Sara jumped. She had not been aware that Annette had already climbed back up the ladder.

"Sara, did you see that dismount?" Seth exclaimed as he climbed up behind Annette. "Wow, Annette, how did you ever learn to do that? Can you teach us how to do it? Geeze, Sara, did you ever see anything like that in your life?"

"No, never," Sara said, trying to sound enthusiastic. She didn't want to admit that she had not seen it at all.

"Sure, I can teach you. It really isn't hard. It's mostly about timing. I've been swinging on ropes for as long as I can remember. But never from trees, and never outside—

and never out over a river. I had no idea what I have been missing. This is just the very best thing I've ever done. Oh, thank you, you two, for sharing your secret place with me! I just can't believe that I could be so lucky. I just love this. Thank you, so much!"

Seth was grinning from ear to ear, and Sara took a deep breath. Annette was genuinely excited about her new experience of flying from the tree house. And Sara could see a new anticipation shining in Seth's eyes.

Sara heard Solomon's voice in her head. *Do not worry, Sara. This will unfold very nicely. Just relax and enjoy your new friend. She will awaken new things in you and in Seth, just as you will awaken new things in her. This will be a wonderful co-creation. You will see.*

"Sara, aren't you going to swing?" Seth's question startled Sara.

"Oh, yeah, I am." Sara said, softly.

Sara took hold of the rope and put her foot in the loop; she held tightly to her knot and jumped into the air. Part of her wanted to lock her legs around the rope and let go with her arms and fly through the air just as Annette had done, but she knew she was not ready for that. But, the idea of learning this new trick did feel exciting, and as the rope swung back and forth, Sara tried to imagine what fun it would be, to be looking at the water while hanging upside-down. She smiled, in happy anticipation of learning something new.

And then, Sara leaped from the rope, and landed a perfect landing on the riverbank.

"Hey, great dismount!" Annette called, from the launching pad, "Good job, Sara!"

Sara felt elated, and shivers rippled up and down her spine. That compliment felt especially good coming from such a rope-swinging expert as Annette. But mostly, it just felt good to feel good.

There you go, Sara. Welcome back. Sara heard Solomon's voice in her head.

"Thanks," she whispered. "It's nice to be back."

CHAPTER SEVEN

Sara stopped by her school locker, stuffed her jacket and book bag inside and pulled out the library book she had been enjoying—and her sack lunch. *Mmmmmmm, smells good,* she noticed. In fact, everything inside her locker smelled like the meat loaf sandwich her mother had made for her that morning. Tucking her library book under her arm, she peered inside her lunch sack to examine its contents. She was happy to see a bright red apple, two chocolate chip cookies, and a sandwich, neatly wrapped. Sara had been so involved in her lunch sack, she wasn't watching where she was going, and she gently bumped shoulders with someone. She looked up, startled, apologizing, into the happy eyes of Annette.

"Hey, Sara, how are you?"

"I'm good. Sorry about running over you. I think I'm way too excited about a meat loaf sandwich."

"A what?"

"A meat loaf sandwich. That's what I'm having for lunch. How about you?"

"I'm on my way to the cafeteria."

"Oh, that's too bad," Sara said, half kidding and half not. Sara knew that today was Tuesday, and that the school hot lunch on Tuesday, for as long as Sara could remember, was soup. "Hearty Vegetable Beef Soup", the luncheon menu proudly proclaimed on the sign in the hallway. But students who had eaten it, through the years, had come to call it "Swamp Stew". It probably didn't really taste so bad, but it looked awful. Long, stringy, overcooked vegetables, that usually could no longer be identified, made up the bulk of this strange concoction, and Sara, and most of the other students, found a way to avoid the cafeteria on "Hearty Vegetable Beef Soup" day.

"Hey, why don't you share my lunch!" Sara blurted, before she realized it. "I never eat all of it, anyway. I was going to sit outside under the tree and read. Wanna come?"

"Oh, I don't want to eat your lunch, Sara, I'll just go check out this Hearty Vegetable Beef Soup. It sounds pretty good."

"It isn't. Trust me. The only people who are in there are those with no ability to discern food from tree bark, like Jimmy, there, he'll eat anything, or those who would starve to death, otherwise. Trust me, Annette. You don't want to go there."

Annette laughed. "Sara, you are a funny girl. Okay, if you're sure you don't mind."

Sara couldn't help but like Annette, and she wasn't sure just how she felt about that. She wanted to like her, but she wanted not to like her. *I'm a schizophrenic,* Sara thought to herself. *Oh, well.*

Sara stopped at the vending machine and dropped in a quarter. She pulled a lever, and a plump bag of potato chips slid down a chute. "Everything goes better with potato chips, don't you think?" She pulled two more quarters from her pocket and bought two cans of orange soda. "There's not much of a selection here," she said to Annette, "but, hey, it's only a quarter."

Sara and Annette found a sunny spot on the school lawn. Sara felt the grass with her hand to make sure the morning dew had dried away, and then she plunked herself down. She tore open the sack, making a paper table between them, and unwrapped the meat loaf sandwich.

"My, that smells wonderful." Annette said, watching Sara carefully unwrapping the sandwich.

Sara's mother had sliced it into two halves. Sara took one piece for herself, and with the wrapper, she handed the other to Annette, being careful not to touch Annette's piece with her fingers. Annette smiled. She could not help but notice what a considerate person Sara was.

Both girls bit hungrily into their sandwiches at the same time, looking at each other as they chomped.

"Oh, Sara, this is the best thing I have ever put in my mouth! However could you stand to give half of it up? This is fantastic!!!"

Sara agreed this was a really good sandwich, but she did think Annette was getting a little carried away about it all. "I'm glad you like it, Annette. But it's only a meat loaf sandwich."

"Well, whatever it is, it is wonderful."

Annette took another small bite and chewed it, and savored it for a long, long time. Sara was certain she had never seen anyone enjoy a sandwich, or anything else, for that matter, as Annette was enjoying her meat loaf sandwich. She didn't reach for a potato chip; she didn't take a drink of her soda; she focused completely on the sandwich until it was gone.

Then the girls finished off the potato chips and drank their sodas. Sara looked at the apple. She realized she did not have any way to split it into two pieces, so she reached into her sack and took out the chocolate chip cookies. Sara and her mother had made them the night before. They made two big batches, so there were plenty for the family to enjoy while watching television, and several to be put in the freezer for lunches and snacks for the next week. Sara offered a cookie to Annette. Annette didn't hold back, in the least. She bit into the cookie and closed her eyes as she exclaimed. "Oh, Sara, this is soooooooooooo good!"

Sara smiled. What in the world is going on with this girl? Hadn't she ever eaten a meat loaf sandwich before? Hadn't she ever eaten a chocolate chip cookie before?

Sara loved chocolate chip cookies. Sara loved just about every kind of cookie. But she didn't love them like Annette loved this one. Not even close.

The bell rang, and both girls jumped a little. "Well, that was a short hour," Sara said. "Time flies when you're having fun."

"Sara, thank you so much for sharing your lunch with me. It was really good."

"Sure," Sara said, standing up, brushing crumbs from her lap. "Anytime."

"Oh, I almost forgot." Annette said, "I can't go to the tree house, tonight. My dad said he has something that he wants us to do right after school, and so, I have to go straight home."

"Oh, okay. Well, then, I'll see you Monday."

"Okay, see ya."

Sara watched Annette running off toward the school building. What a strange mix of feelings moved within her. Annette was not easy to figure out. She was so pretty, and very smart, and truly nice, and from the big city, and way too excited about meat loaf sandwiches and chocolate chip cookies.

Oh, well, Sara shrugged, and went inside the building.

CHAPTER EIGHT

Sara opened her eyes, and lay in her bed for a moment, wondering what had awakened her. Her alarm clock was quiet. She rolled over and looked at it. 7:45. *Oh, yeah, it's Saturday,* she remembered. She could hear her mother clanging around in the kitchen. Her mother had a, not so subtle, way, when she thought it was time for Sara to get up, of making just enough noise that it was not likely that Sara could continue to sleep. And then, she always pretended to be surprised when Sara would emerge into the kitchen.

"Well, good morning, Sara! Did you sleep well?"

"I guess." Sara sighed, still in the process of waking fully.

"I'm going to the grocery store in a little bit. Would you like to come with me?"

"Yeah, I guess." Sara agreed. She had no great desire to accompany her mother, but she knew there would be many bags of groceries and that her mother could use some help. And, it was sort of fun to get to offer her input as to what might be good for the family to eat for the next week. Her mother sometimes seemed to get stuck in the monotony of cooking, day after day, week after week, and so, she was always probing Sara for another idea of what they might try. And, of course, Sara had her favorites, which seemed to win out, for the most part.

Sara and her mother moved systematically through the grocery store, up one aisle and down the next. "Oh, Sara, I forgot the onions. Would you run back and get a couple for me, Honey? Yellow ones, not too big. Oh, and a quart of ice cream. Vanilla. We'll make a pie."

Sara went back to the produce department. She knew right where they would be; the yellow onions had been on the same shelf in the same place for as long as Sara could remember. She chose two medium sized onions and headed for the frozen food aisle. Sara playfully tossed the two onions back and forth from hand to hand pretending that she was juggling. And as she came around the corner of the frozen food aisle, she was looking up at the onions crossing in midair instead of where she was going, and she ran right into someone's grocery cart, dropping both onions at the same time. Sara scrambled to retrieve her onions, which had rolled several feet across the floor.

"I'm so sorry!" she exclaimed. "I should have been watching where I was going."

"Sara!" A startled voice said.

Sara stood up, and there was Annette, standing over a shopping cart filled to the very top.

"Hey, Annette, how are you doing?" Sara could not believe it. This was the second time, in only two days, that she had run into Annette, while being totally preoccupied with food. *She must think I'm crazy,* Sara thought.

"I'm good," Annette said, turning her cart around and walking away from Sara. "I'll see you at school."

That's odd, Sara thought. *I wonder why she's in such a hurry.*

As Annette hurried down the aisle, Sara noticed that her shopping basket was filled to overflowing. There were cans of food, lots of them, and cardboard cartons of frozen dinners—the kind you put in the oven and warm up—and on the very top was a big bag of chocolate chip cookies.

Sara found her mother, and added her only slightly bruised onions and quart of ice cream to the cart. They stopped at the deli section, and bought some cheese and a few olives, and then went to the checkout counters at the front of the store. Sara wanted to hurry. She hoped that she would catch a glimpse of Annette, and maybe get the chance to see her mother.

I don't think she wants me to meet her mother, Sara thought. *Maybe that's why she rushed off.*

But when Sara and her mother reached the checkout counter, Annette was nowhere to be seen. Sara didn't know why she was so interested in all of this. And something about it felt a little bit like spying. *I should just mind my own business,* Sara thought. *It's clear, Annette doesn't want me sticking my nose in. So, I'll just mind my own business. That's what I'll do.*

CHAPTER NINE

"Do you believe in ghosts?" Annette just sort of blurted it out.

Sara and Seth both looked up with surprise.

"Well, yeah, I guess," Sara said. "I mean, I've never actually seen one, but I guess I believe that they are real. Do you?"

"What about you, Seth, do you believe in ghosts?"

Seth wasn't sure of the best way to answer Annette's question. He sensed, from the serious look on her face, that she wasn't kidding about this. "What do you mean by 'believe in' something," Seth stalled.

"What do you mean, 'what do I mean?'" Annette answered, sharply. "I think that's a pretty simple question."

Seth could tell he had hurt her feelings, but he did have an important point that he wanted to make: "Well, I mean, lots of people believe in things, just because other people tell them that it is so. My grandpa says if you tell people anything enough times, before long, they'll start to believe it, whether it's true or not. He says people are gullible, like sheep. They'll follow along with anything you want them to believe. And I don't want to be like that. So I decided, a long time ago, not to take anyone's word for anything. So I don't accept anything as true until I've proved it, to myself, with my own experience."

Sara watched Seth as he spoke with such clear determination. *He is certainly sure of how he feels about this,* she thought.

"And so, since I've never actually had a personal relationship with any ghost, I cannot say, for sure, from my own experience, that I believe that they exist. But I do think that it might be possible. I mean, I've had other weird experiences...."

Seth's voice trailed off as he realized that he might be opening doors into subjects he wasn't really ready to discuss with Annette. Sara looked up, sharply. She hoped that Seth wasn't going to tell Annette about Solomon.

Annette noticed Sara's sudden interest. "Well, what about it, Sara? Do you believe in ghosts?"

"Well," Sara stalled, "I guess I do." She remembered the night Solomon visited her in her bedroom after Jason and Jimmy shot him. She hadn't really thought about

Solomon being a ghost, that night; she had been so glad to see Solomon. But thinking about it, now, she realized that most people, if they had seen what she saw, would probably say they had seen a ghost. But she sure wasn't ready to tell Annette what she knew about Solomon.

Sara and Seth looked at each other. Both of them knew that if anything would fall into the category of ghosts, Solomon was most likely it, but they both held back, uncertain about confiding in their new friend about their special secret. Sara wished that they could just forget about it and swing on the rope.

"Well, do *you* believe in ghosts?" Seth asked, looking hard at Annette's serious face.

Annette looked at Seth, and then at Sara, and then at Seth, and then back at Sara.

Sara and Seth sat quietly, each wanted to hear Annette's answer.

"No, I just wondered if you did," Annette answered, abruptly. "Hey, let's swing." And without taking her usual time to carefully execute her perfectly calculated leap from the platform on the swinging rope, Annette grabbed the rope and leaped off the platform as if she couldn't get out of there fast enough.

"Well, what was that all about?" Sara said, as soon as she thought Annette was out of earshot.

"I think we should tell Annette about Solomon." Seth said, excitedly.

"No, Seth, no! I don't think we should tell her. Promise me, Seth, that you won't tell her."

Annette looked back at them and waved.

"Sara, are you sure? I mean, I think..."

"Please, Seth, promise me?"

"Okay."

CHAPTER TEN

As Sara made her way to school the next morning, her thoughts kept coming back, again and again, to Annette. Her decision to mind her own business seemed to have already faded from her mind. She saw Seth, a little more than a block away, walking out ahead of her. "Hey, Seth!" she called out, "Wait up!" *I don't know why I'm yelling,* Sara thought. *He's too far away to hear me.*

But Seth stopped and turned around and waved, and began walking toward Sara. Sara ran to meet him.

"Hey, Seth," Sara said, out of breath, "Have you seen Annette's mother?"

"No," Seth said, pausing, awkwardly. "I can't say that I have."

"Oh, I was just wondering..." Sara felt a slight twinge of guilt as she realized that she was not keeping her promise to herself to mind her own business.

They crossed the bridge on Main Street, and as they stood in the crosswalks, waiting to cross the street, a big, black, shiny car passed in front of them.

"Isn't that Annette's dad's car?" Sara asked. "I heard them talking in Pete's Drugstore about what an expensive car it is. Wow! That's the prettiest car I've ever seen!"

The large, long, black, sleek-looking car, with lots of shiny chrome, turned down the street to the grade school. It was hard to see who was inside because of the very darkly tinted windows, but Sara thought she could see a man driving, probably Annette's father, and someone quite little in the front seat, and one person in the back seat. Probably Annette.

"Don't you think it's strange that we haven't seen her mother?"

"No, not really."

"I mean they've been here over a month now. I saw Annette in the grocery store, with a whole cart full of...."

"Sara, I just remembered I forgot something I need for class. You go ahead. I'll catch you later." Seth suddenly turned around and began running back down the road toward his house.

Sara watched him running about as fast as she had ever seen him run. "Seth, wait!" she called out. But Seth did not look back.

Sara did not believe that Seth had forgotten something. It was as if something she had said had upset him. Why had her questions about Annette's mother upset him? This was weird.

Sara didn't see Seth all day long. It was strange not to run in to him between classes, even once. It was as if he was deliberately avoiding her. That made no sense, but his strange behavior that morning hadn't made any sense, either.

After school, Sara felt an urge for a candy bar, so she stopped by Pete's Drugstore on her way to the tree house. *I'll get one for everybody,* she thought, reaching deep into the bottom of her bag for a handful of coins that always seemed to end up in the bottom corner of her bag.

"I think it is so sad that those sweet little girls have no mother," Sara overheard a woman commenting from the soda fountain area, "isn't that just the saddest thing you ever heard?"

Sara's ears perked up. Who were they talking about?

And then, she knew. They were talking about Annette and her sister. Annette's mother was dead! Sara's heart began to beat faster.

"Well, that certainly is sad. I didn't know." Sara heard someone else say.

"I don't think many people know. But Sam Morris, the new man, moved in last year, lives over on the old Thacker place. He's the new foreman over on the Wilsenholm ranch, and he works with my husband. Anyway, he told my husband that he and his boys helped Mr. Stanley and his girls move in to a new house up on the river. Took 'em all of one weekend and a few evenings, too, I guess. Says he never saw so much furniture and so many boxes in his whole life. He said he was glad to help out, though. Said they're all real nice people. And he said that they were told, then, that first day, about Mrs. Stanley's death. Such a sad, sad thing."

Sara could not believe her ears. Annette's mother is dead. And Seth knew about it! Why didn't he tell her? Why would he keep such a secret from his very best friend? Sara left the candy bars in the middle of the counter and wheeled out of the drugstore.

I'm never going to talk to him again! Annette can be his new best friend. His only friend, for all I care. I am never going to speak to him again! Or to her, either!

Sara stared blindly ahead as she walked toward her house. She passed Thacker's Trail without even looking toward it. There was no way she was going to the tree house, today.

"Sara," Seth called out to her. "Sara where are you going? Don't you want to swing with us?"

Sara looked straight ahead. She knew that Seth knew that she had heard him, but the very last thing Sara felt like doing was talking with Seth, or Annette. She broke into a run, and ran all the way home.

CHAPTER ELEVEN

Sara sat restlessly on the edge of her bed. Her pretty room felt confining, like, there wasn't enough air. She opened her window and sat on the large windowsill looking out into the back yard. The yard was covered with a blanket of bright colored leaves. Her eyes rested on the old tire swing her father had made several years ago by tying a rope through an old truck tire. It made a great swing. Big enough for two if you didn't mind being squished together. Sara hadn't been in that swing since Seth had built the tree house. The old tire swing had seemed so inferior to the fantastic new swinging rope Seth had hung in the tree house; there was really no comparison to the thrill of the ride. But, today, that old tire swing looked like a forgotten old friend—and Sara was feeling pretty much the same way. She slipped out of her window, something her mother had asked her a hundred times not to do, and pulled herself up into the old tire. It was not possible to swing very high because the tire kept spinning on the single rope it was tied to. But it was fun to twirl round and round while moving back and forth. Rather mesmerizing. Sara closed her eyes to intensify the effect. Round and round, back and forth. Round and round, and back and forth.

Sara.

Sara heard Solomon's clear words from above.

She looked up into the tree, and, sure enough, there sat Solomon, his feathers blowing gently in the wind.

"Oh, hi, Solomon. I'm surprised to see you here."

I'm surprised to find you here, Sara. You haven't been in this old swing in a very long time.

"I know." Sara said, softly. "I just felt like it."

Solomon sat quietly by. Sara twirled round and round.

They're waiting for you in the tree house, Solomon said.

"I don't care." Sara spun gently around in the swing.

Solomon was quiet. He never pushed Sara into talking if she wasn't ready.

"Solomon, why didn't Seth tell me he knew that Annette's mother was dead? I mean, it's not like he didn't know I was interested. I asked him straight out if he'd ever met her. And he lied to me, Solomon. I just can't believe it. I thought we were friends."

Seth had quite a struggle with that one, Sara. Annette asked him not to tell anyone. And she specifically asked him not to tell you.

"And so, he cared more about not hurting her feelings than he did about mine? That's just great!"

Well, Sara, I guess that is one way of looking at it. Or you could say that he feels more secure in his friendship with you, and he felt you are standing on more stable footing, right now, than Annette is. In other words, he may have felt that Annette has quite a lot to deal with, right now.

A tear rolled down Sara's face, and she wiped her face with her sleeve. "Well, why didn't she want me to know?"

Well, Sara, I suspect it is because she has noticed that people behave differently toward her once they find out. She doesn't want people to feel sorry for her, Sara. She's like you, a proud, hearty girl who truly prefers to feel happy.

Sara swallowed hard. She felt embarrassed about how she had been feeling. It was bad enough that that overpowering feeling of jealousy seemed to overtake her, again and again; that is such an icky feeling. But now, mixed with that feeling of jealousy, she felt an equally uncomfortable feeling of guilt about feeling jealous—and now, a feeling of real sadness, and even more guilty feelings, about poor Annette, moved through her.

Another tear rolled down Sara's cheek, as she thought about sweet Annette, buying frozen dinners by herself, and eating store bought chocolate chip cookies.

You see, Sara, that is the very reason Annette didn't want Seth to tell you about it. She has begun to rediscover how lovely life can be, again. But each time a new friend finds out about her mother's death, she has to go back and relive all that sadness, again, through their perspective. You can see why she might want to avoid that.

"Yes." Sara wiped her nose and looked up at Solomon.

"Solomon, I don't know what's going on with me. I feel so awful."

Solomon listened, quietly, waiting for Sara to try to clarify what it was she wanted to know.

"I mean, it seems like ever since Annette got here, I've been feeling bad. I mean it's not her fault, or anything. I just..."

Well, Sara, I'm sure you'll feel better soon; you are naturally such a happy girl. But it might be worth taking a little bit of time here, to receive some benefit, or clarity, from all of this negative emotion.

Sara wiped her nose and looked at Solomon. She could feel a familiar calming reassurance coming from him. He had helped her feel better so many times.

Remember, the first thing that a strong feeling, or emotion, is telling you, is that this thing that you are thinking about, really matters to you, very much. The stronger the feeling, the more it matters. The second thing your emotions are telling you is whether, in this moment, you are a match to this important thing that you want.

Sara knew what Solomon meant about matches. She had had many conversations with him about that. She remembered how Solomon had explained about Law of Attraction, and birds of a feather flocking together.

In other words, Sara, if you are experiencing a very strong feeling that does not feel good to you, like fear or anger or jealousy or guilt, or blame... those feelings mean that you are thinking about something that matters very much to you—but that the thoughts that you are having are not a match to what you really want.

Sara listened.

However, when you are experiencing a very strong feeling that feels good to you, like love or appreciation or joy, or eagerness... those feelings mean that you are thinking about something that matters very much to you—and, in this moment, the thoughts that you are having ARE *a match to what you really want.*

Negative emotion is not a bad thing, Sara. It helps you to recognize what you are doing with your thoughts. You don't think it is wrong when your sensitive fingertips tell you that the stove is hot. That sensitivity saves your fingers from being damaged. And negative emotion is a similar indicator. It just lets you know that to stay focused longer upon this thought that doesn't feel good, really isn't good for you.

Sara stretched her feet out to the ground and slid down out of the swing. She sat on the ground and put her face in her hands. "Oh, Solomon, I know all of this. You've told me this, like, maybe a thousand times."

Solomon smiled. *Well, not quite a thousand times, Sara.*

"Oh, Solomon. Seth must think I'm awful. What should I do?"

There is really nothing to be done. Nothing has happened that needs to be fixed. Your friendship with Seth will be an eternally evolving thing, and nothing has changed to make it less, in any way. I expect that the three of you will be the very best of friends.

Sara wiped her nose, again, and looked up at Solomon. "But Solomon, I liked things the way they were. I don't want...."

I remember when you felt that very same way about our friendship, Sara. You didn't want Seth to know about us.

Sara looked up at Solomon, and wiped her nose, again. She remembered that, too.

And yet, look at how nicely that is turning out, Sara. I haven't noticed your feeling unhappy about you and I sharing our friendship with Seth.

Sara was quiet. Solomon was right about that. Sara felt no discomfort about Seth loving Solomon, and Solomon loving Seth. She loved watching them interact with one another. She loved the delight that they brought to each other. Her relationship with each of them is better because they now know each other.

Sara, you have been a very healthy girl for a very long time.

"Yes!"

Can you imagine, telling your mother, "Well, since I have been so healthy for so many years, I've decided to be sick for a few years, to allow more people to be healthy"?

Sara laughed. "No, Solomon. That's silly."

Silly, because you understand that other's are not sick because you are getting more than your share of wellness. You understand that your experience of wellness has nothing to do with theirs.

Sara smiled. "I get it."

Sara, always remember there is plenty of love to go around. Seth's appreciation of Annette in no way detracts from his appreciation of you. In fact, if anything, it makes it more. Just look for the very best feeling thoughts that you can find about your two dear friends.

Sara drew in a deep breath of fresh air. She felt so very much better. "Okay, Solomon. I'll think about it. Thanks."

Solomon lifted into the air, and flew away.

CHAPTER TWELVE

The next day, after school, Sara sat high in the tree house waiting for Seth and Annette to join her. She shifted from place to place trying to get comfortable. She felt uneasy. She was still feeling embarrassed about her behavior the day before, and she wasn't quite sure what she would say when they got there.

She had been trying to find good feeling thoughts about Seth and about Annette, but her thoughts kept turning back to Annette and her family. She could not imagine what it would be like if her own wonderful mother were missing from their family. That thought was just too awful to think about.

"Whew!" She exclaimed quietly to herself. "These thoughts do not feel good. I shouldn't be thinking about this."

"Anybody up there?"

Sara heard Annette's voice calling from down below.

"Yes, I'm here," Sara called back down, jumping to her feet and self-consciously pulling her shirt down, smoothing out the rumples in it. She felt flustered, as if she had been caught doing something she shouldn't have been doing.

Sara saw Annette put a tin box in the bucket at the base of the tree. Then she stuffed her coat in around it and scurried up the tree ladder.

"What's in the box?"

"Oh, just some stuff I brought from home. Some things I wanted to show you."

"Oh. Do you want to wait for Seth? He should be here any minute."

"He's not coming today," Annette answered. "I saw him, earlier, and he said he'd catch us tomorrow."

Sara felt that bad feeling rising up within her again. *He probably hates me,* she thought.

"You are the best friend Seth has ever had, Sara!" Annette said, clearly.

Startled, Sara looked at Annette. It was as if Annette knew what she was thinking.

"He said he had been watching for you all day long, but for some reason, just hadn't been able to find you, and he asked me to be sure to tell you that he would see you tomorrow."

"Okay, thanks," Sara said.

She felt much better.

Annette untied Seth's rope, and pulled the bucket up onto the platform.

"I'll get that." Sara said, standing up to secure the rope. Annette took her coat out of the bucket, and spread it like a blanket on the platform, and then, she carefully placed the tin box in the center of her coat.

"How pretty that is." Sara said, softly, getting down on her knees next to Annette to get a closer look.

Annette tugged on a chain, which was around her neck, pulling up a pretty locket that Sara had never noticed before. She opened the locket and retrieved a very small key, which she put into the tiny lock in the tin box.

Sara sat, waiting, feeling as if a remarkable treasure was about to be revealed to her. Annette's movements seemed so precise, as if she had practiced them a hundred times. She turned the tiny key in the lock, and the lid on the box sprang open. Sara squealed, as her body spontaneously jumped back in surprise.

Sara felt embarrassed at her seeming disrespect for what seemed to be a ceremonial opening of this precious box, but Annette didn't seem to notice. She seemed removed from everything that was going on around her, in her now, while completely absorbed by whatever was in this pretty little box.

Sara sat back and took a deep breath, and deliberately tried to relax.

Annette's delicate little fingers picked through the contents of the box. "This is my mother." Annette handed the glossy picture to Sara.

Sara did not look at Annette's face as she reached out to take the picture, and she wasn't sure she really wanted to look at the picture, either. She had no idea what the appropriate response to any of this should be, and she, very much, did not want to do or say the wrong thing.

"That's me, with her." Annette said, breaking the awkward silence.

Sara looked at the picture. It was a very worn and tattered picture with dog-eared corners and a big crack running right through the middle of it. It was very difficult to see the face of either the well-dressed lady or the little girl in the photo because it had been taken from a distance, and the people in the photo appeared very tiny. And, in a very young child's hand writing, in what looked to be crayon, were large printed letters: "ME AND MOMMY".

"That's the first picture that was taken with me and my mother. I wrote that on there when I was, like, four years old." Annette laughed. She took the picture from Sara and put it back in the box. Sara still didn't say anything.

"This is us about a year later. My dad says my mom was always trying to get him to carry the camera and take pictures everywhere we went, but he said he hardly ever did. He always said that people spend too much time looking back at what was and not enough time enjoying what is. I think he's sort of sorry, though, that he didn't take more pictures."

Sara looked at the picture. Again, it was impossible to see the faces of the lady or the little girl. There was a big fountain in the picture with a woman sitting on the edge of it, while a little girl appeared to be walking around the edge.

"My dad said I loved that fountain. It was in the park near our house. He said I would get up on the edge of it and run around and around, and around, and no matter how long I was allowed to do it, I always cried when we had to leave."

"This is all of us." Annette said, handing Sara another picture.

"Wow," Sara said, before she could stop herself. "That's the prettiest picture I've ever seen."

"My dad said my mother insisted that we have at least one family portrait. My dad never got close enough, in any pictures that he took, to see anybody's face. My mother used to say they might as well be strangers in the pictures, because no one would ever be able to tell. But, my dad said that the picture should tell a bigger story. That it should be about what is happening, not so much about who it is happening to."

"My mom liked this picture." Annette said, handing Sara another picture.

Sara looked at the beautiful faces in the picture. Annette's mother was very beautiful. Pretty, long, dark hair, like Annette's, and big, dark brown eyes. Annette's father was very handsome, too. And her little sister was like a miniature version of Annette, a very pretty little girl. "Annette, you have such a beautiful family."

Sara stopped short, wishing that she had not said that. She felt so sad that this beautiful family was no longer together. Tears welled up in Sara's eyes, and she looked the other way so Annette would not notice.

"Well, that's the only professional picture we have. And just about the only picture where you can see any of our faces. Oh, except this one." Annette pulled a newspaper clipping from the box with a picture of a little girl, who looked to be about three years old, and a great big dog. It was a close-up picture of the faces of this odd pair. The dog was licking the little girl's face.

Annette laughed. "I wish I could remember this. My mother said we were walking in the park, and I had been eating an ice cream cone and had it all over my face. This big dog just walked right up to me, and started licking my face. My mother said a photographer from the newspaper was sitting on a bench, nearby, eating his lunch, and saw the whole thing, and took the picture. It was in the newspaper the next day. My mother said she was so embarrassed. Finally, somebody got a close-up picture of her little girl's face—and a dog is licking food from it."

Sara read the caption: *Little girl won't wash her face so she gets a lickin.* Both girls laughed.

"She said she could only hope no one she knew saw it. My dad loved it. He bought every newspaper he could find that day and sent one to everyone he knew. He said that a picture should tell a story, and that was a story worth telling. He said, A PICTURE IS WORTH A THOUSAND WORDS."

Annette sorted through the little box, pulling out picture after picture, quietly describing each one. Sara began to relax, occasionally asking, "Who is this? Where was this taken? Wow, is that your house?"

And then Annette closed the box and locked it again with the little key. The girls sat looking at the box. Sara felt as if she had been watching a movie that she didn't want to end.

"So, if your father were to take a picture of the two of us sitting here, what do you think it would look like?"

"Well," Annette laughed, "first of all, he'd get as far away from us as he possibly could, like, maybe way high up in the tree. And he'd try to get as much of the tree house in the picture as possible, with the bucket and pulley, and the swinging rope, too, I imagine, and you and I would look like tiny little specks sitting down here on the platform."

Sara laughed. It was fun to imagine the picture.

"And the caption would read," Annette paused and looked right into Sara's eyes, "And so, it *is* possible to be happy again."

Thrill bumps bumped up all over Sara's body. Tension that she didn't even realize was still binding her, lifted off. And she sat there feeling as wonderful as she had ever felt in her life.

"Sara, I wanted you to understand that I am really okay about all of this."

Annette looked at her watch. "Oh, I've got to get going," she exclaimed. "I had no idea we have been here so long. Sara, let's talk more tomorrow."

"Okay."

Sara watched Annette hurry down the path. She felt so happy to have this dear new friend.

CHAPTER THIRTEEN

After school, the next day, the two girls sat perched high in the tree house. Sara thought it was odd that Seth, again, had told Annette he would not be at the tree house. And even though it did not feel comfortable to Sara that he stay away again, she was happy for the opportunity to continue her conversation with Annette.

"Oh, is that your father I see high up there in the tree trying to get a picture of us wee things down here?" Sara teased, trying to bring back the mood from yesterday.

Annette laughed. "No, I think that's him in the helicopter up there. The top of the tree is way too close."

The girls sat quietly. Sara wished that they could just pick right up from where they left off yesterday, but twenty-four hours had passed, and neither of them were at the clear, high place they had been the day before.

Annette broke the silence. "Someday, maybe I'll write a book about it."

"About what it's like for someone..?" Sara stopped in the middle of her sentence. She just could not say the words.

"Not so much about what it's like to have *someone you love die*," Annette did complete Sara's sentence. "But to help the other people, close to those people, feel more comfortable to be around them."

Did Sara understand Annette correctly? Her book would not be written to help people who had lost loved ones, but instead, to help the people who knew the people who had lost the loved ones?

"Sara, the hardest thing, after a while, I mean, is the way people act around you, once they hear. They don't know what to say. And, in truth, it really doesn't matter, very much, what they say, because no matter what they say, it all feels bad: If they don't know about it, you think they should have known. If they do know, you wish they didn't. If they try to soothe you, you hate how sappy they are, and if they don't try to soothe you, they seem uncaring. They are in an impossible situation. And I'd like to write a book that would, somehow, help that."

Sara leaned back against the tree and looked at her new friend. She could hardly believe what a dear person Annette was. She didn't think she had ever heard anything so unselfish in her whole life.

"Oh, Sara, don't look at me like I'm noble or anything. It's not like that."

Sara blinked her eyes and sat up straight, looking at Annette, wanting to understand what was going on in her mind. Sara could not find her place in this.

"My best friend, Caroline, said, 'I'm glad it was your mother and not mine.'"

Sara winced.

"At the time, I thought that was just about the meanest thing that anybody could ever say to anybody. But I don't feel that way now. Oh, it may have been better if she hadn't said it, but, for heavens sake, how could she not feel that way. And what in the world is wrong with saying what you feel. And, what could be more natural than to feel that way. My friend did nothing wrong. She didn't mean anything bad by it. And, most of all, she was in an impossible situation where there really was not anything that she could have said that would have made me feel better.

"Once, I heard a lady in the grocery store telling someone that it wasn't so bad when a wealthy family looses a parent, because they can afford to hire people to help, but that a real tragedy is when a poor family loses a parent, because then the little children have to go without good care."

Sara squinted her eyes, as she winced.

"I know," Annette smiled. "And when she left her cart for a little while, I pinched her bread and punched holes in her tomatoes."

Sara laughed. "She got off easy."

"No, Sara, that's my point! People aren't being unkind on purpose. They just don't know what to say. And the reason they don't know what to say is because nothing that they might say would make any real difference. It isn't something that anybody can do for you. My Mom, says...."

Annette stopped, suddenly, as if she hadn't meant to say something. Then she began... "I guess I want two things, really: I want people who are hurting, from the death of someone they love, to understand that they will feel better again; and that it doesn't have to take a long time—and, for those around them to just relax and wait for that to happen. Everybody's just too worried about this death thing."

Sara looked up, suddenly, and stared hard into Annette's face. She could hardly believe her ears. That sounded exactly like something Solomon would say. Without ever even meeting Solomon, Annette knew it, too.

"Not too long after my mother died, my aunt brought a beautiful white, fluffy kitten to us. My dad didn't like that she brought it. I think he was really mad at her for doing it. My aunt put the kitten down in the middle of our living room floor, and the little cat jumped right up into my mother's favorite chair; my mom loved doing needlework there by the window. The cat curled up on the cushion and laid her head on her paws, as if to say, 'There now, this is where I belong.'

"My dad pushed the cat off of the chair, and then that silly cat jumped up onto another chair, and another, and onto the sofa; I think she climbed on every piece of furniture in the house. I remember chasing her all over the house. I don't think there was one single place that she didn't sniff. And when she was finished, she jumped right back into my mother's chair.

"I picked her up and put her in my lap, and she licked my face with her scratchy tongue, and purred. I remember feeling so happy. I remember laughing and laughing. It felt so good.

"I heard my father scolding my aunt in the other room. He said, 'A thousand kittens won't bring her mother back!'

"And my aunt said, 'I'm not trying to bring her mother back—I'm trying to bring Annette back.'

"And I remember thinking. *Yes, I'm back.*"

Sara felt thrill bumps bumping up all over her body. She could hardly believe the things she was hearing from Annette. She knew, without any doubt, that it was time to share her secret about Solomon, with Annette. She could hardly wait to find Seth to tell him that she had changed her mind. She wanted to tell Annette everything. And, mostly, Sara wanted Annette to meet her friend, Solomon.

CHAPTER FOURTEEN

Sara left school as quickly as she could. She hoped that she would meet up with Seth on the way to the tree house so that she could tell him her new decision about telling Annette about Solomon. But Seth and Annette had already arrived and were, in fact, waiting for Sara.

"Hi, Guys," Sara said, breathlessly, as she climbed up into the tree house.

"Hi, Sara," Seth grinned. He was glad to see her.

The three of them sat awkwardly looking at each other. Then all of a sudden, Annette blurted out, "My Mom says that I should...." Her voice trailed off. She looked down and fidgeted with the locket hanging around her neck.

Sara and Seth looked at each other. "What in the world?..."

"She said that you are not like most kids. She said that you understand death. She said that you have a dead friend, too, and that your dead friend knows me, too."

Sara and Seth looked at each other. Neither of them knew what to say.

"Well," Sara began. "Our friend isn't exactly dead, anymore. I mean, he was dead, but now he's not."

Annette squinted her eyes and looked at Sara, trying to make sense of what she had just heard. "He was dead, but isn't now?"

"See, he was alive," Seth tried to help, "Solomon, that is, that's his name, but then Sara's little brother and his friend killed him, with a gun."

Now Annette's eyes were open wide. "Killed him with a gun? These boys killed this man, Solomon, with a gun?"

"Oh, no, Annette, Solomon's not a man. He's an owl."

"Your dead friend is an owl?"

Sara and Seth looked at each other. This was coming out all wrong. "Well, he's not dead now. But he is an owl. A talking owl."

Annette took a deep breath and leaned back against the tree. "Oh, I see."

Sara and Seth sat quietly, looking at each other and then at Annette. This was not going well at all. *What if Annette doesn't believe us? What if she just thinks we're crazy? And worst of all, what if she tells somebody else what we've told her?* Sara wished that they hadn't tried to tell Annette about Solomon. But it was too late to take it back.

"What do you mean that this Solomon owl was dead but now is alive?"

Sara took a deep breath. "Well," she said, hesitantly, "it's sort of a long story, but here goes." She absentmindedly pushed the sleeves up on her sweater as if she were really getting ready to go to work on something. Seth sat down next to Sara, looking at her, intently. He folded his long legs up, and leaned forward, as if he were eager to hear the interesting story that was about to be told. Sara could feel him next to her, and she felt a feeling of comfort wash over her as she realized that, this time, the two of them were in this together. She didn't feel so far out on a limb, in exposing her weirdness to their new friend, as she had before, when she was all alone explaining all of this to Seth.

So much had happened in Sara's life since the meeting of her dear friend, Solomon, that she had a hard time finding the beginning place. She had learned so much from Solomon, and, in many ways, it felt unnecessary to even try to go back to the beginning. She wasn't sure she could, even if she tried.

Seth could see that Sara was having a hard time getting started, but he felt that it was best that Sara tell the story because, after all, Solomon was Sara's friend, first.

Sara remembered the snowy day she had found Solomon sitting on a fence post on Thacker's Trail, and her amazement when he spoke to her as if owls sitting on fence posts talk to little girls all the time. Sara thought about how smart Solomon is, and how he has answers to every question that she could ever ask. And she remembered how Solomon had shown her how to fly, and had taken Sara and Seth on wonderful night flights around Sara's little mountain town.

Her mind was spinning. She just couldn't decide where to begin. She wanted Annette to know everything about Solomon, all at once. But, what was the best way to begin?

Sara, Sara heard Solomon's voice in her head. *Who I am is who I am, and no amount of explanation will change that. Annette will adapt to the idea of me, just as you did, and just as Seth did. All is well here. Just begin.*

Seth saw a feeling of calm wash over Sara, and he relaxed and leaned back against the tree. He could feel that all was well, and he could feel Sara's inspiration beginning to flow.

"Well, Annette, I guess I'd like to begin by just explaining to you who Solomon is."

"He's an owl, right?" Annette chimed in, quickly.

Seth and Sara looked at each other, and grinned.

"Well, yes, he is that, but oh, Annette, he is so much more! Solomon says that we are all much more than we think we are." Her eyes studied Annette's face, carefully, watching for any sign of alarm or disbelief.

"Go on," Annette encouraged.

"He says that while we are here, in these bodies that we can see and feel, that there is another part of us that is much older, that never dies—and that that part of us is really here with us all of the time. Solomon says that some people call that part of us our Soul, but Solomon calls it our Inner Being."

Annette sat, quietly.

"Solomon says our Inner Being lives forever. And that sometimes it expresses itself in a physical experience. He says, it's not like being alive or dead, because there is no such thing as dead. It's just that sometimes that Inner Being comes into a physical form and sometimes it doesn't—but it is always alive and always happy, just the same."

"Go on," Annette encouraged.

"We are, like, extensions of that older, Inner Self. And when we are really feeling wonderful, that means that we are allowing more of that Inner Self to flow through us, in that time. But when we don't feel so good, you know, like when we're afraid or mad, or something—then we aren't allowing who we really are to shine through."

A tear pushed out of Annette's eye and rolled down her cheek.

Sara looked at Annette. She didn't know if she should go on or not.

"My mom told me almost the same thing, Sara. She came to me in a dream, and she told me that she would talk to me, if I wanted—but only when I'm happy. She said I wouldn't be able to hear her unless I was happy. When I woke up, I cried and cried. I didn't think it was possible, now that she was dead, to ever be happy again. And so, I thought that I would never get to talk to her again.

"But then, my Aunt brought us that little kitten, and the kitten licked my face with her scratchy tongue, over and over again. And while I was laughing, I heard my mother's voice. She said, 'She's a beautiful cat, Annette, why don't you call her Sara.'

"I was so happy. Because then I understood what my mother had meant. I mean, I was still real sad when I thought about her dying, and everything, but in that moment, I realized that if a little kitten could play with me and distract me from my sadness enough that then I could hear my mother, that there must be lots of other things that I could think about that would help me hear her, too."

Sara and Seth listened, in amazement. Sara wanted to hug her and kiss her. She wondered what she had ever been worried about. Annette had already come to understand, through her own life experience, much of what Sara had wanted to tell her.

The three of them sat huddled in a small circle, quietly looking at each other, eyes filled with happy tears of recognition; recognition of one another and of Well-being. Sara stretched her arms out, putting one around Annette and the other around Seth. Seth and Annette reached out and did the same thing. They sat huddled, with hearts singing.

I think that's my cue, Solomon said, perched on the top branch of the big tree. *There could never be a better time than this.* And, in a swift and graceful dive, from high overhead, Solomon descended on his three featherless friends, landing right in the middle of their huddle.

Room for one more? he asked.

"Solomon!" Sara squealed, "We are so glad to see you!"

Well, my fine featherless friends, it is nice to be seen.
Hello, Annette, it's very nice to formally meet you.

Annette's mouth dropped wide open. She looked at Sara and then at Seth and then at Solomon, and then at Sara. Her mouth was moving, but no words were coming out.

Sara and Seth sat, beaming. They recognized how Annette must be feeling, because it hadn't been very long since they had first heard Solomon speak.

"Well," Sara said, "it's like they always say: a talking owl is worth a thousand words."

Seth and Annette laughed hard.

Well, kids, I can't stay. Solomon said. *I'm late for my Spanish lesson. But I'll be back tomorrow. We can talk then, if you like. Hasta la vista.* And, quick as a wink, Solomon was up and away.

Sara and Seth burst out laughing.

"Not only does he talk, he talks in more than one language?" Annette said, laughing so hard tears were running down her face.

"Apparently so," Sara said, still laughing. "There's never a dull moment around here. Always perfect, and always changing."

The three of them sat motionless on the platform.

"Wanna swing from the tree?" Seth finally said.

"Nah," Sara said.

"Nah," Annette said.

CHAPTER FIFTEEN

Sara and Seth, and Annette sat on the floor of the tree house waiting for Solomon to join them.

"We could swing while we wait," Seth offered.

"Nah, I'm good," Sara said.

"Me, too," Annette agreed.

Sara's mind was still racing. She had barely slept the night before, and had barely noticed anything that had happened at school today. A question had occurred to her that she just couldn't wait to ask Annette.

"Did you say that your mother told you about us?"

"Yes."

Sara wanted her to go on.

"She comes to me in my dreams. Not every night, just sometimes. Oh, there he is!" Annette jumped to her feet pointing up at the sky.

Sara and Seth jumped up, too.

"He is huge!" Annette exclaimed, as she watched Solomon circling in the sky above the tree house.

Sara and Seth looked at each other, and grinned. It had been a long time since Solomon had made such a grand entrance. Sara watched Annette, and felt that familiar feeling of thrilled anticipation as Solomon circled closer and closer, down to the tree house.

And then, plunk. Solomon landed on the railing. *Well, hello, my fine featherless friends....*

Annette squealed her delight.

How are you today, Miss Sara? Solomon looked deeply into Sara's eyes.

"Never better!" Sara felt wonderful.

That seems perfectly clear to me. And Seth?

"I'm good, Solomon. I'm very good."

Yes, Indeed. And, Annette, we are very happy that you have joined us. How are you today?

"I'm good, too, Solomon. And I am so happy that you all have included me. I can't believe how lucky I am. I feel so lucky."

We all feel that way, Annette. It is wonderful to be together. We are birds of a feather, you know—and birds of a feather flock together!"

Annette laughed.

Sara, what would you say is the most significant thing you have come to know since we have been flocking together? Solomon asked.

Annette and Seth laughed.

Sara looked at Solomon. Why was he asking such a big question of her? Why didn't Solomon begin by explaining to Annette, in the way he had explained to Sara and then to Seth? She had hoped that Solomon would show Annette how to fly, as he had shown Sara, when she first met him, or Seth, when he first met him.

She squinted her eyes, trying to find the answer to this very big question. It seemed like there were so many important things that she had learned from Solomon. So many things had happened in Sara's life since meeting Solomon, and he had helped her and Seth through so many situations, it didn't seem possible to sift through all of that, right now, and decide the one most significant thing.

Solomon, I don't....

Sara, Solomon interrupted. *I'll give you a hint. The way you know the thing that is most significant is that the emotion you feel around it is very, very strong. So, if you can remember the most powerful emotions—you'll discover what is most important.*

"Do you mean good emotions, or bad emotions?" Sara asked. This was fun. She loved learning from Solomon, in this way.

I mean, good or bad. When the feeling is strong, whether it feels good or bad, it always means it is important. But, often, it is

easier for you to remember those powerful bad feeling emotions. They
are often the first indicator that something important is happening.

"So, you're saying that if I can remember the very
worst thing that ever happened to me, or the very worst feelings that I have ever felt, that then, I will know the thing
that is most significant?"

That's right.

"Well, Solomon, when you put it that way, it's easy to
answer. Because the worst that I have ever felt, in my whole
life, was when Jason and Billy shot you. And you were
bleeding. And then you closed your eyes. And I thought you
were dead."

Annette winced, and folded her arms tightly around
herself.

Sara, I was dead! Solomon said, dramatically. *At least
in the way you mortals look at it. Your father buried my rumpled
pile of moth eaten feathers in the back yard. Don't you remember?*

A blast of laughter shot out of Sara's mouth.
Solomon's blatant disrespect for death had caught her off
guard. And sitting there, talking with someone about their
own death, while they were, in this moment, so very much
alive, somehow took the sting out of this solemn subject.

*Yes, I foresee many joyful conversations about death ahead
of the three of you.*

Sara and Seth, and Annette, all laughed hard.

"Solomon, you sure do have an strange perspective about things."

Me, have a strange perspective? I think it is you mortals who have the strange perspective. Think about it: Every one of you knew, when you came into these wonderful physical bodies, that you would be only temporary tenants in them. And every one of you, even now, understands that you will not remain permanently in them. You all believe that you will die, for you know of none who have not. And yet, you insist on worrying about death, and pushing against it. You do not see it as the beautiful, normal, miraculous thing that it is. Instead, you see it as something unwanted, and hated; you see it as a penalty. And when you find someone within your society that you truly despise, you give them the "Death Penalty." It is no wonder you are confused about this subject.

The three of them stared silently at Solomon. He was right. Not one of them knew anyone who didn't openly fear the idea of death. It was a solemn, uncomfortable subject.

Most people are so afraid of death they do not allow themselves to live. And that is particularly unfortunate, since there is no such thing as death. There is only life and more life.

"I want to know everything, just the way you do, Solomon." Sara said.

Well, Sara, you already do know. I'm just here to help you remember it all more clearly. You will be remembering one thing at a time, and all in good time. The three of you are doing extremely well in your remembering of who you are.

Well, I'm off. You kids have a good time swinging on your rope. Good day! Solomon lifted, powerfully, into the sky and was gone.

Annette looked at her two new friends. She felt happier than she could ever remember feeling. "My mother was right," she said. "You do know about death."

"We know," Sara said. "We just have to keep remembering that we know."

CHAPTER SIXTEEN

Sara left her jacket on the cement pilings at the end of the Main Street bridge and climbed out into her "leaning perch", and basked in the warmth of the Saturday afternoon sun. She loved this place. And she loved this river. Sara loved this river more than just about anybody had ever loved this river. She loved it in the spring, when it nearly overflowed its banks and lapped up over the crossing log that she loved to scurry across. She loved it in the winter, when ice crept from the edges toward the center until the icy water silently flowed beneath the snow-covered ice. She loved it in the summer, when it was warm enough that you could roll up your pants and wade in the shallow parts of it. And, she loved it in the fall, like now, when beautiful leaves made colorful rafts, floating downstream to places unknown. Sara often pretended that she was small enough, like Thumbelina, her favorite character from bedtime storybooks, to ride the tiny leaf raft and discover the wonderful and unknown worlds that lay between her small mountain town and the giant ocean, downstream. Sara propped her chin on her knees and thought about such a ride, and smiled.

Mother would just love that, she thought, sarcastically, remembering how often her mother had voiced her concern about Sara's obsession for this river. Sara's pleasant thoughts about the river disappeared as she remembered her mother's irrational concern.

Parents are such worrywarts, she thought. *They just worry about everything, when, really, there is nothing to worry about, at all.*

Sara remembered her amazing encounter with this river. She always felt such a strange mix of feelings when she remembered falling off the crossing log, or rather being knocked off the crossing log by a big, over-eager dog. In the short time that she was actually in the water, she had moved from sheer terror, to a sort of relaxed resignation that she probably was going to drown; to the amazed wonder at the beauty of the river as she had floated on her back, for miles, downstream; to the triumphant realization that, no matter what, all really was well in her life. Sara knew that her strange ride on that fantastic river had somehow changed her. It was the beginning of her understanding that all really was well.

"Sara! Sara! Sara!"

Sara was jolted by the sound of her little brother's voice.

"Did you hear that Samuel Morris almost drowned in the river? Sara! Sara! Did you hear?" Jason shouted as he ran toward her.

Sara crawled back off of her leaning perch, watching her frantic little brother running toward her and holding his hat on at the same time.

"Samuel?" Sara said, under her breath. "Who is Samuel Morris? Oh, no," she gasped, as she began putting it all together in her mind. *That's Seth's little brother.*

"How do you know that? Who told you? Where is he? Is he all right?" Sara's questions came in such a constant stream that Jason couldn't answer one before the next one was blurted out on top of it.

"They were talking about it over at Pete's Drugstore."

"Well, tell me!" Sara shouted, angrily, grabbing Jason's wrist and looking him hard in the face. "What did they say?"

"I don't know!" Jason shouted back, yanking his arm back, defensively. "Geeze, Sara, what's it to you?"

"I'm sorry, Jason, I didn't mean to grab you. I mean..." Sara's voice trailed off. She wasn't about to explain to her little brother the wonderful friendship that she had discovered with Seth, Samuel's big brother. She couldn't explain that, in a hundred years of trying. And, anyway, this wasn't the time to begin it. "Just tell me what you heard."

Jason looked stubborn. He didn't like the way Sara often tried to boss him around, and he liked knowing something that she wanted to know. It made him feel powerful.

"Please, Jason, what did you hear? Please, tell me!"

"Just that this stupid little kid had tried to build a raft, and that he was trying to float down the creek, but when the creek dumped into the river, the raft turned over, and he fell off, and that the current was too swift for him. Oh, and something about his brother pulling him out, just in time."

Seth! Sara thought. "Is he... are they all right?"

"I don't know, Sara. That's all I know." Jason ran off toward home.

Sara stood in the middle of the bridge, not knowing what to do next. Should she go to Seth's house and just knock on the door? That seemed bold. She had never been inside of Seth's house. *Maybe I'll just walk past and see what's happening, there.* She turned the corner and headed toward Seth's house.

The street looked pretty much like it always looked. Sara couldn't see anyone; there were no cars around, and no people, either. The house looked quiet, like usual. Nothing seemed to be stirring, anywhere.

Sara's heart was pounding hard in her chest. She wanted to find her friend and feel his reassurance that everything was all right, but she didn't know where to go. She rarely saw Seth on the weekends. She didn't know what to do. Sara began running toward the drugstore. Maybe they would still be talking about it. Maybe someone, there, would know what happened.

Sara blasted through the front door of the drugstore of this old dilapidated building. The familiar smell of medicines and perfumes, combined with that of hamburgers and onions cooking on the grill, greeted her. She saw a handful of people sitting at the soda fountain, chatting eagerly with each other about something. She hid behind the magazine stand, so as to not be detected, and moved as close as she dared, and strained her ears to hear.

"Stupid kids. They just don't seem to understand the dangerous currents of that river. They think it's a playground, only there to entertain them." Sara heard an elderly woman complaining.

"Well, that's just the way kids are, these days, you know. They think everything is a game. You can hardly get them to work, anymore." Pete said, wiping the counter with a stained and greasy looking rag as he spoke.

Sara winced a little as she listened. *Crabby old bags,* she thought. *What happened? Get to what happened.*

"Well, this isn't the first kid to nearly drown in that river. Didn't the Henderson girl nearly drown, too? What's her name, Sara, isn't it? I heard that she fell in and nearly drowned. Somebody should do something about those kids playing on the river. They just shouldn't be allowed to do that."

Sara shrank behind the magazine rack. Her heart began to pound so hard she was afraid they would hear it. She wanted to run and hide, but there was nowhere to go. She would just die if they caught her hiding there.

"Her mother told me that she had told that girl to stay away from that river a thousand times, but it didn't do any good. I still see her dangling out over the river, from time to time. Well, I'll tell you, if they were my kids, they wouldn't be playing around the river. I'd give 'em plenty of things to do. I would keep them so busy they wouldn't have time to be messin' around that river, and if they didn't mind me, well, I'll just tell you, they'd be a mindin' me," a great big woman said.

Sara looked out her from her hiding place. *If I were your kid, I'd just build a raft and float as far away from you as possible,* Sara thought. *Away from all of you. You're just mean, awful people who don't know anything.*

The front door banged open, and three men came in.

"They'll be all right," Sara heard one of them say. "The older one got pretty cut up on a piece of barbed wire, but it didn't look too bad. He'll probably be all right. If he doesn't bleed to death on the way."

Sara's heart jumped into her throat. *Seth!* she thought. Her eyes filled with tears. She felt as though she couldn't stand it another minute.

"He's a strong swimmer, that kid. I mean, I'd of thought twice before jumping in there. That's a mean current."

"Did the doc stitch him up?"

"Doc's out'a town. Had to drive 'em over to the hospital in Fowlerville."

Hospital! Seth's in the hospital! Sara couldn't stand another minute of it. She ran from behind the magazine rack, and flew out the door. No one noticed her, at all. She ran down the street with tears streaming down her face. She could barely remember a more awful moment in her life.

She ran across the Main Street bridge, down the river trail, down the secret paths that she and Seth had made, and up Seth's wonderful tree ladder to the tree house. Being in their secret place, knowing that he was hurt, and probably scared to death, where she couldn't see him or soothe him, or help him, was just the most awful thing that Sara could even think of. She put her face into her hands and cried and cried, and cried.

"Solomon. Solomon. Where are you Solomon? I need you. I need you to help Seth. Solomon, where are you?"

Solomon was circling high above the tree house. Sara opened her eyes, and squinted up at the sky, but her eyes were so clouded with tears, she could hardly see anything at all. She wiped her face on her sleeve, and sniffed to try to clear her nose. Her head felt all stuffy. No air would pass through her nose, at all. It had been a long time since Sara had cried so hard that she felt like this. It did not feel good.

But seeing Solomon, circling in the sky over her, gave her an immediate feeling of relief.

Sara had learned a great deal from this wonderful magical owl. And the most important thing that she had learned from him was about the powerful Law of Attraction. *A law more important than all other laws combined,* Solomon had explained. *A law that says, "That which is like unto itself, is drawn."*

Sara knew that the terrible way that she felt, right now, was not, in any way, a match to the feeling of Well-being that Solomon was about. And so, she knew that when she was feeling this awful, that Solomon could not help her, could not even be with her—for Solomon was a teacher of Well-being.

Sara sat up straighter and pulled the rubber band out of her hair, that was holding her ponytail. She held the rubber band with her teeth, and combed her fingers through her hair, and tied her ponytail again with the rubber band. She wiped her face on her sleeve, breathed deeply, and tried to find some thoughts of Well-being, as Solomon had taught her so many times before. Sara knew that in order to return to her feeling of Well-being, that she must release these traumatic thoughts and replace them with thoughts of Well-being. But, this is not an easy thing to do. Not when your best friend in the whole world is in trouble.

Sara watched as Solomon circled in the sky. His big wings flapped powerfully as he would climb up, up, up, and then he would glide softly down, down, down. Simply by watching his mesmerizing circles, Sara began to feel better, almost tranquil—and then, Solomon dropped softly onto the platform beside her.

All is well, Sweet Sara, Solomon began.

"Solomon, thank you for coming. Samuel fell in the river, and Seth saved him, but I think Seth is hurt, and I don't know about Samuel."

Solomon listened as Sara explained.

Then Sara caught herself, remembering that she did not have to explain any of this to Solomon. For Solomon, Sara had come to know, knew about everything. And surely he would know about Seth. For Sara and Seth, and Solomon, were the very best of friends.

It seems you were swept up in the trauma of the drugstore crowd, Sara. Have you forgotten that Well-being abounds?

Sara looked at Solomon. "Oh, yeah, I guess I did," she said, softly, feeling embarrassed.

Sara, don't be hard on yourself. It's a normal human thing to do, to let the reality of the moment, that you are observing, set the tone for the way that you are feeling. When someone you love experiences something that you do not want for him, it is normal to feel bad. But remember, Sara, you are one who offers unconditional love. And one who understands and lives unconditional love—is able to feel good under all conditions.

Sara smiled as she recalled the many hours she and Solomon and Seth had talked about unconditional love. And how it's easy to feel good, or to feel love toward someone or something when everything is going well, but the true test of unconditional love is to let it flow completely through you even when things do not appear to be going well.

Seth and his brother are both just fine, Sara. And I suspect the wounds from the barbed wire will mend rather easily. But the wounds that a worrisome town, or frightened and concerned parents, will inflict, well, those can be the more troubling wounds.

Sara knew exactly what Solomon meant. She had experienced a pretty good dose of that, herself, as she was hiding behind the magazine rack in the drugstore.

You'll be a big help there, Sara.

"What do you mean?"

You will be one person, undoubtedly the only person, who will not dramatize the negative experience. You will be the one stable person in Seth's life who will stand before him knowing completely the Well-being of his experience.

Sara felt a strong river of guilt wash through her, for she had not been maintaining her knowledge of Seth's Well-being. She had easily been swept away in the current of fear and trauma.

Don't feel badly about your worrisome thoughts, Sara. Your fear only points out your tremendous love for your friend. But you found your balance, quickly. In fact, you are stronger in your knowledge, right now, than you would have been if you had not lost your footing for a time. For your desire to hold your balance is much stronger now.

Sara felt SO MUCH BETTER!

Sara, show your love to your friend by giving no attention, at all, to Seth's injuries.

"But, Solomon, won't he feel like I've abandoned him?"

Sara, I am not suggesting that you withdraw your attention from your friend—only withdraw your negative attention. Give Seth your attention, but only focus on aspects of his experience that feel good to you while you focus on them.

I believe that very much good will come from this, Sara. All is well, Sweet Girl. I'll talk with you later.

Solomon lifted, with his powerful wings, and flew away.

Sara breathed, deeply. Solomon had given her a great deal to think about. She wondered when she would see Seth. And she wondered what she might say to him. She felt relieved that she would not see him today, because she wanted time to think about all of this, and to practice having only positive thoughts.

CHAPTER SEVENTEEN

All day long, as Sara made her way through the crowded hallways between her classes, she continued to search for Seth. *I hope he's okay,* Sara thought, sadly.

She walked down the stairway from the fourth floor, to the third floor, to the second floor, and as she rounded the last turn, leading to the first floor level of the school building, she saw Seth walking slowly down the stairs. She slowed down and walked several steps behind him, watching him. His backpack was awkwardly hanging across his right shoulder. For a moment, Sara wondered why it was not on his back, the way he always wore it, and then she noticed a large bulky bandage on his left arm, which seemed to wrap his entire arm, from his shoulder right down to his finger tips.

Sara gulped, realizing, from the size of the bandage she could see, that Seth's left arm must have sustained some serious injury. And then, as he turned to go out the big front doors, Sara gasped, right out loud, as she saw another bandage covering almost the entire left side of Seth's face. She started to call out to him, wanting to soothe him. Or maybe she wanted him to soothe her? But she stopped short.

Holding onto the stair railing to steady herself, as her knees felt like they might buckle right out from under her, Sara remembered Solomon's wise, clear words. *You will be one person, undoubtedly the only person, who will not dramatize the negative experience. You will be the one stable person in Seth's life who will stand before him knowing, completely, the Well-being of his experience.*

The last thing that Sara wanted was for Seth to see the alarm she was feeling. Sara was glad that she hadn't bumped into Seth, all day. She really needed more time to find her place. How in the world was she supposed to be a stable person and not dramatize his negative experience, when half his body was covered in those awful looking bandages? How could she pretend that everything was just the same as it was before?

Solomon, Sara called out in her mind, *I need your help. I need you to help me focus on something good about Seth's bandages.*

Sara, those wonderful bandages are assisting in the healing process. Underneath those bandages, are intelligent cells of Well-being. Those cells are now summoning Source Energy, in

106

more powerful ways than usual, to assist in the healing process. The human body is a remarkable thing, Sara. It is resilient and flexible, and hearty—so just imagine the bandages removed and your beautiful Seth restored anew.

Sara smiled. Solomon had a way of always making her feel sooooo much better.

"Thanks, Solomon!"

"Hey, Seth, Wait up!"

Seth was not moving very fast, but he was already half way across the parking lot. Sara ran to catch up.

"Hey!" Sara said, as she caught up with Seth.

"Hey!" Seth said looking the other way.

"I heard you were an amazing swimmer and that those swift currents didn't hinder you, one bit," Sara said, wanting to emphasize the most positive point she could think of about the extraordinary experience Seth had had, since she had seen him last.

Seth was quiet.

"And your fast thinking and fast action saved Samuel's life!"

Seth was still quiet.

"And Mrs. Carlisle's hair piece fell in the banana pudding and got tangled in the mix master, and they had to throw out all the pudding." Sara grinned. She had no idea why that came out of her, but she was happy to notice that Seth was smiling, too.

He laughed. "Sara, did that really happen, or did you make it up?"

"No, I swear, it really happened! Seth, you know I would never lie to you. Not about important things, like pudding, anyway."

"Yeah, right." Seth laughed. "Well, all right then. That's good."

"It's good to see you, Seth. I missed you."

"Yeah, I missed you, too, Sara. I guess it'll be a few days before I'll be swinging from the tree, and I can't go there tonight because...." He stopped, not wanting to explain that he was supposed to go to the doctor's office to have his bandages changed.

"No biggie," Sara chimed in. "We'll catch up in a few days. I have about a million things to tell you, but nothing that can't wait. I'll see ya later, Seth."

Seth turned the corner toward his house. Sara felt as if she had successfully completed an obstacle course, where any number of things could have gone terribly wrong, but, didn't. She smiled a little. She felt pretty good about what had just happened. It wasn't a perfect conversation; she knew that. But she had somewhat succeeded in not dramatizing what most would call a negative experience. She wanted to uplift Seth. And she hoped that she had.

Good job, Sara. Sara heard Solomon's voice in her head.

"Thanks," Sara said, softly. "Thanks for your help."

CHAPTER EIGHTEEN

It felt strange going to the tree house, knowing that Seth would not be there. Annette had said she probably wouldn't be there, either because her dad wanted her to meet the new housekeeper, or something like that.

Sara decided to stop by Pete's Drugstore to buy a candy bar. She stood in front of the candy display trying to decide which one to buy. She chose one, then changed her mind and put it back. She chose another, then, changed her mind again and put it back. She laughed, under her breath, at her indecision. Through the years, Sara had happily devoured hundreds of candy bars. But today, none of them called to her. "Oh, well, you look pretty good," she said, choosing a Hershey's Bar with almonds. She stood at the counter, waiting for Pete to come and take her money.

Pete was behind the soda fountain talking with people perched on the spinning bar stools. He didn't seem to notice that Sara was there, and he went on with his story, wiping the counter, absentmindedly, as he spoke.

"Well, the young one is going to be fine," Sara heard a woman in a white dress say. "But that older one. He's gonna have some serious looking scars. Such a pity. He was such a handsome lad. Hmm, kids. They never learn."

Sara left the candy bar on the counter, and walked out of the drugstore. She had completely lost interest in any kind of candy bar. She walked, wearily, to the tree house.

She sat high in the tree house leaning back against the tree, with her knees pulled up to her chest, and rested her chin on her knees. It was a warm fall day, and the sound of the wind moving through the trees, and leaves falling everywhere, all around her, muted all other sounds in her world. She breathed in, deeply.

Well, Solomon, wherever you are. It's just you and me, today. Just like old times. Sara stretched out on her back on the floor of the tree house looking up into the great old tree. Every now and again a stronger gust of wind would whish through the trees, and a shower of golden leaves would rain down around her. Sara wondered how long it would take for the leaves to completely cover her body. She smiled at the idea of Seth climbing the ladder to find her still body completely buried under the fallen leaves. *I wish he were here,* she thought, as a stronger feeling of loneliness swept over her. *Oh, Solomon, why do people get scars?*

Sara heard a heavy rustling in the leaves, overhead, and then a flutter of leaves floated down around her, and then, Solomon plopped down on the tree house floor right next to her. Sara sat up, laughing and combing leaves out of her hair with her fingers.

Do all people get scars, Sara?

"I don't know. Don't they?"

Well, Sara, that's quite a variable. Some do and some don't. It really depends on their level of resistance. It depends on how well they are allowing the natural Well-being of their physical bodies. You see, your bodies are made up of trillions of cells, each holding the vision of their perfection and of their perfect place in the perfect whole.

"Solomon, do these cells think? I mean, you make them sound like little tiny people, or something."

They have different intentions, and they focus their consciousness differently than you do, but they are consciousness, just like you are, and they do think. They understand. They have powerful knowing. And, most importantly, each of them holds a clear vision of their perfection, and clearly and constantly asks for whatever is required to maintain that never-ending perfection. In fact, Sara, the Life Force that your body experiences, comes because of the never-ending asking of these cells.

"Wow! But, Solomon, if these cells know who they are and hold a vision of being perfect—then how come people get sick, or how come people get scars?"

It is only because people sometimes hold themselves in places of worry or fear, or anger, where they are not allowing the Energy— that the cells are asking for—to pass purely through them. Their worrisome thoughts cause a sort of static in their bodies that doesn't allow the Energy to flow through in a nonresistant way.

You see, Sara, every time anyone, even a tiny little cell in your body, asks for something—it is always given. So, when a body is injured, in some way, the cells closest to the injury calculate exactly what they need to regain their balance—and they send out immediate requests. And, instantly, the Energy begins to flow, and all other aspects of the body begin to respond, too. Special helping nutrients of all kinds begin making their way through the body, and the natural healing begins, immediately. And when the person, who lives in this body, is happy or eager, or appreciative— then the healing is allowed. But if that person is sad or angry, or fearful— the healing is hindered, or resisted.

"Hmmm. But, I guess it's not the easiest thing to feel happy or appreciative when you've just had an accident."

Agreed. It is more difficult then. But even so, with some effort, anyone could do it, especially if you understand that your body has a natural healing process. However, Sara, what goes wrong, for most people, is that instead of paying attention to their own situation and being aware of their own allowing, or resisting, and then noticing their own results —instead, they are keeping score of many other people. And when they see others not healing, they assume that that is just the way it is when a person is injured. They do not consider whether that person is allowing the healing Energy to flow. Most people do not understand the power of healing that is within their very own body. And so, instead of feeling strong and hearty, they feel guarded and vulnerable. It's rather odd, too, with so much evidence of healing around them.

"So, are you saying that if Seth feels happy, that he won't get scars?"

That's right, Sara. His body remembers how it was before the injury. And, if allowed, can restore itself to that perfection.

"But, Solomon, look at my scar." Sara pulled up her pant leg exposing a long narrow scar down the front of her shinbone. "I was standing on a tree branch, and it broke. And I got this big old scratch when I fell out of the tree. How come I got this ugly scar?"

What do you remember about that day?

"Well, I tore my pants, and my leg was really bleeding. My mom was mad at me because I wasn't supposed to be up in the tree. She threw my pants away; she said they were too ruined to be fixed. And then, she put some stinging red medicine all up and down my leg. That really hurt. She said it would kill the germs. And then she wrapped a bandage around my leg. Around and around. It made it look like my whole leg was hurt."

What else?

"Well, that Saturday, our family went to the swimming pool, over in Fowlerville, and I wasn't allowed to go in the water. And I remember how hot it was, and my bandage was all stuck on my sore. It really hurt when my mother took it off. I couldn't even take a bath, for a long time. And..."

That's enough, for now, Sara. Looking back on all of that, would you say that you were feeling more happy and eager and appreciative, or angry and disappointed, and sad?

"Well, that's not hard to answer. I was pretty mad at myself for falling. I should have been watching what I was doing. And, I was mad 'cause I ruined my pants; and I knew I would be in big trouble for that, and for falling out of the tree, and for even being in the tree in the first place."

Sara sighed a big sigh. Just talking about it took her right back to how she felt on that unhappy day.

Sara, ordinarily I would not encourage you to spend so much time remembering something that didn't feel good to you, but since you are asking about this most important subject of allowing your physical body to heal, it is important that you understand what it is that you do that keeps it from healing.

"Well, Solomon, are you saying that if a person could just feel good, that their injuries would heal and wouldn't even leave a scar?"

That's right.

Sara sat, quietly rubbing the scar on her shin. This scar had been there for over two years. It was hard to imagine it not being there.

Feeling good, Sara, is the answer to all good life experience.

Sara absentmindedly continued to rub her leg, trying to remember more about that day she fell from the tree: A family, from the city, had come to have lunch and spend the day with Sara's family. They came once or twice every year, and Sara never looked forward to it. It always meant extra chores in getting the house ready for company, and so much extra time in shopping and preparing the food. And while her parents always enjoyed their friends, Sara did not enjoy their children, at all: A boy, her little brother's age, and Kay, a year older than Sara. Kay was a city girl, with very pretty clothes, and, as far as Sara could see, a very snooty attitude. She made constant comparisons between her perfectly lovely city life and Sara's obviously substandard country life. Sara always did her best to be polite in the face of what always felt to Sara like deliberately rude comments, but when Kay remarked how unfortunate it was that Sara's town didn't have a market where suitable food could be purchased for special occasions, Sara's patience was suddenly gone. She remembered turning on her heels and running out into the back yard, determined to do the least city-like or ladylike thing she could think of to do. And, in an attitude of fury, she climbed up into the tree, hoping never to have to look this disgusting girl in the face, ever again.

Sara. Thinking back, is it not easy to see that falling from the tree was an accurate match to the way you were feeling?

"Yeah, right," Sara laughed. "That was pretty clear."

And so, when you consider the way you were feeling, and the amount of resistance that was within you before you fell out of the tree, is it not easy to understand that the resistance would be greater still AFTER *you had fallen from the tree? For then you are hurting; your pants are torn; your mother is angry.*

Although Solomon was still explaining, Sara's own thoughts temporarily drowned him out. Sara could still see Kay's gleeful face looking down at her as she lay there on the lawn, with the wind knocked out of her. "It was as if every rotten thing Kay had been saying about our family, all day long, was true. I was the perfect proof of it, lying right there on the ground in front of her."

Solomon was quiet. He knew that Sara understood, perfectly.

Sara looked up at Solomon, and sighed a big sigh. "Well, it's no wonder we get scars. It's not easy to let the Well-being flow."

Solomon laughed. *Well, Sara, it gets easier and easier. But it does take some practice.*

Okay, Solomon, I guess I'd better get going. Thanks.

You are most welcome, Sara.

"Solomon," Sara said, quickly, wanting to catch Solomon before he flew away. "Was Seth in a bad mood, and that's why he got hurt when he tried to save Samuel?"

Actually, Sara, Seth was in a very good place when Samuel fell into the river. It was because he was feeling so good—and was so clearly connected to his Guidance System—that he was inspired to take that path on his way home that afternoon. A less connected person would not have found Samuel, to begin with.

"But, Solomon, I don't get it. If Seth was so connected to his Guidance System, then why did he get hurt so badly?"

Sara, don't let the drugstore crowd influence you to negative conclusions. From broader perspective, things have worked out very well.

"But, Solomon, couldn't Seth have saved Samuel without getting hurt?"

Certainly, Sara. That is a possible thing. But you must not assume that something terribly wrong has happened here. Wonderful opportunities are sometimes masked by seeming difficulties. It is only when you understand that Well-being truly does abound, that you are able to discover the life-giving nuggets that are all around you.

"Well, okay, Solomon. You are always right. It just seems to me that...."

Sara, do you remember when your furry friend knocked you off of your crossing log and into the river?

"I'll never forget that."

And how do you think other people feel about that incident, Sara? Do you think they are happy that you were pushed into the river, and that you floated, for miles, downstream?

"No, Solomon. They think it was awful. They think I was stupid for being on the crossing log, to begin with. They don't think I should be near the river, at all."

And what about you, Sara? Are you sorry you were pushed into the river?

Sara's face lit up in a big smile of understanding. "No, Solomon. I'm not sorry I fell into the river."

Why not? Why don't you feel the same way that others do about your raging river experience?

Because, when I got out of the river, that day, instead of being afraid of the river, and what might have happened, I just felt powerful. It was like, everything that everybody was always saying about the river, to try to scare me, turned out to be untrue. I felt like I was safe, anyway, no matter what they all thought. Solomon, that's when I knew that the river was not a threat to me. I think that was my first real taste of my own Well-being. I wouldn't take any of that back, for anything, Solomon. Not any of it."

So, are you telling me that sometimes when you are looking at something from the outside, you might not really understand its true value?

Sara smiled. Solomon was so wise. He understood everything.

And that only the person who is living the experience can really know the full value of it, or the reason for it?

Sara, Seth's experience, like yours, will provide so much value for him. Value that will continue to unfold for many years to come. Well-being always abounds, Sara, no matter how it looks at first, or to those on the outside.

Sara smiled. She felt wonderful. "Thank you, Solomon. Thank you, so much!"

CHAPTER NINETEEN

Sara could hardly wait to meet in the tree house, again, with Seth and Annette. She was brimming with her new understanding about Well-being, and she was eagerly anticipating Seth's fast recovery. She could hardly wait to tell Seth about the cells in his body and how they know exactly what to do, and that he would be back to his perfect rope swinging self, in no time. Sara was experiencing a fantastic new feeling of vitality and enthusiasm.

As she moved from class to class, she watched for Seth, and for Annette. She practiced, in her mind, the conversations they might have. She felt so excited to tell them everything that she had come to understand, about how, sometimes, when things look as if they have gone terribly wrong—that everything is really all right.

Sara saw Annette coming toward her and moved to the edge of the hallway to wait for her. Annette did not look happy.

"What's wrong?" Sara blurted, wishing, immediately, that she hadn't started the conversation on such a negative note.

"Oh, Sara. I just saw Seth, and he says that his parents have forbidden him to go to the tree house. They don't want him near the river. Oh, Sara, what are we going to do?"

Sara stood, stunned. She just couldn't believe what Annette was telling her.

Don't take score too soon, Sara. Sara heard Solomon's voice in her head. *You have stood in many places that looked worse than this one—and things have always worked out, before. Don't give in to negative speculation.*

Annette looked as if she were about to cry. And, while Sara was still shaken by Annette's terrible news, Solomon's words had soothed her, somewhat, because Sara knew he was right.

"Annette, don't worry," Sara tried to console her friend. "We've had experiences sort of like this, before, and everything turned out all right."

"I guess," Annette said, flatly.

"No, really, Annette. Mr. Wilsenholm owns all of the land where the tree house is. I think he owns about half of the town. Anyway, when he found out we were swinging from his trees, he freaked out, and he ordered the trees along the river to be cut down."

"You're kidding?" Annette said. "All of those lovely trees? That's just awful."

"Yes, but, Annette, that's what I'm telling you. He didn't cut them down. He changed his mind. Solomon says we can change anything around to the way we want it—just by changing our own thoughts."

The bell rang and the girls both jumped. It was hard to pull away from this intense and important subject and go back to the boredom of the next class. Sara wanted to explain to Annette how Mrs. Wilsenholm, after witnessing Sara's amazing rescue of her kitten from high in the tree, had convinced her husband that Sara and Seth were really very safe in the trees. How there had been so many examples of things seeming to be going terribly wrong, and how Sara and Seth, with Solomon's guidance, had been able to change their thoughts, which changed the way they felt—which brought about wonderful solutions. She wanted to tell Annette about the time that Seth's family was being forced to leave Sara's town because his father had lost his job at the hardware store, and how happy Sara and Seth had been when Mr. Wilsenholm had offered him a job as the foreman of his ranch. And, then, how *awful* they had felt when Seth's father refused to take the new job, but, then, how he had changed his mind once he understood the whole situation better. In the short time Sara had known Seth, there had been so much evidence of Well-being in the face of what initially felt like crisis.

"Everything will be all right," Sara tried to console Annette. "Let's meet at the tree house after school."

"I hope Solomon can help us fix this, Sara."

"It will be okay," Sara said, again. "You'll see."

"Oh, I hope so," Annette said, walking backwards, in the direction of her classroom.

I hope so, too, Sara said, under her breath, realizing that she was not feeling quite as confident as she was trying to sound.

CHAPTER TWENTY

As Sara walked toward the tree house, she got madder, and madder. She had been thinking about what Solomon had said, about how the human body heals, and how when you feel good there is less resistance so that the body can heal even faster. *Seth's parents are so stupid,* Sara thought. *Instead of helping Seth to feel good, they are punishing him by forbidding him to do the thing he loves the most in the whole world. They are going to keep him from healing!*

"Sara, wait up!" Sara heard Seth's voice calling from behind.

She felt embarrassed that Seth would catch her right in the middle of the most negative thought that she had, maybe, ever thought. She tried to change her mood, quickly, but the look on her face gave her away.

"Sara, what's wrong? You look like your cat just got run over for the tenth time, or something."

Sara laughed. "No problem. My cat has unlimited lifetimes."

"I guess Annette told you; I've been temporarily exiled." Seth tried to sound playful.

"Yeah, I heard."

"Sara, don't worry about this. We've been through way worse things than this. It'll blow over. I can't do much fancy swinging from the rope, with these bandages, anyway."

Sara looked at Seth. She wanted to look into his eyes to see if she could tell if he was really feeling as good as his words sounded. He didn't seem bothered, but, instead, he seemed calm and confident.

"I know. You're right, Seth. Everything will be all right. I know it will."

"Sara, you and Annette have fun over there. I'll see you later."

Sara felt relief. She was very happy that Seth was not angry at his parents, and that he didn't seem to be holding himself in a state of resistance that would keep his wounds from quickly healing.

Sara ducked off the road onto the path leading to the tree house, and Seth continued on down the road toward his house, but it just felt wrong that Seth was not going to the tree house. Sara felt very sad.

As she came around the last bend of the trail, to the edge of the water, she could see Annette, standing out on the platform of the tree house, looking up into the treetops. Sara left her things at the base of the tree and climbed up the ladder to the platform where Annette was standing. This all seemed so wrong. Seth should be here!

It seemed like only yesterday that she and Seth were happily swinging from the rope in their very own tree house, sharing a deliciously private friendship and amazing secrets, and now, in the blink of an eye, Seth is banished from the tree house, and even from Solomon, and here is this new girl, instead. Sara had not liked it that Seth had invited Annette in, to begin with, but now, it seemed that Annette had replaced Seth. Seth was gone, and Annette was here.

"Hi, Annette." Sara said, flatly. When she heard her own voice she wished she had tried to sound more cheerful.

"Hi, Sara," Annette replied. She didn't sound any more cheerful than Sara.

"Well, here we are," Annette said.

"Yeah," Sara said.

Solomon sat, perched high in the treetops on the other side of the river, watching the girls settling in, and once they were comfortable, he flew across the river, and glided softly to the platform. Plop! *Well, hello my fine, fearless, friendly, freedom-loving, female, featherless friends!*

The girls laughed. "Solomon, are you always this happy?"

Well, yes, Annette, I guess I always am. The alternative is unacceptable.

Sara looked at Solomon. She admired his consistent philosophy of always looking for things to feel good about. She wished she could be more like him.

"Unacceptable?" Annette responded. "You make it sound like it is always your choice?"

It always is.

As Sara watched Annette's intense face, pouting in response to Solomon's reply, she remembered so many times that she and Solomon had exchanged the very same words. Sara could easily guess what Annette would say next, because Sara had said it, herself, so many times:

"But, Solomon, sometimes things just happen that you can't control, that make you feel bad!"

I know that it sometimes feels that way, Annette, but that is never true. In time, you will come to understand that you can always control the way you feel.

Sara knew Solomon was right about this, for she had proven to herself, so many times, that she could change her focus, and therefore change the way she was feeling. But, as she listened to Annette talking with Solomon, she couldn't help but think about Annette's mother dying, and how awful that would be. And how impossible it must be to focus on something else in order to feel better.

"But, Solomon," Annette protested.

Sara pulled her legs up close to her chest, and rested her chin on her knees. She closed her eyes to try to brace herself in readiness for the painful, heart wrenching words that Annette was about to speak about the death of her mother.

"But, Solomon," Annette continued, "how can Sara and I feel good about swinging from this wonderful tree house, when our friend, Seth, who made this tree house, isn't even allowed to play here with us, anymore?"

Sara opened her eyes, and stared at Annette in amazement. The terrible uncontrollable thing she was talking about was not the death of her mother, but Seth's banishment from the tree house!

Solomon smiled deeply into Sara's eyes as he enjoyed this extraordinary understanding washing through her.

Sara didn't know how, but somehow, Annette seemed to have left the pain of her mother's death behind her. Solomon had talked for many hours with Sara about the power of turning your attention to other life-giving things in order to feel good in the now, no matter what—but Sara had never really understood it so clearly as she did now.

She sat back against the tree, eager to hear Solomon explain to Annette, as he had explained to Sara, so many times before, about staying connected to the Stream of Well-being no matter what is happening in your experience. And, about how you have control over the way you feel—because you have control over what you give your attention to.

Solomon began: *Everything that happens is a good thing.*

Both Sara and Annette looked hard at Solomon. Neither spoke. He surely did have their attention.

The things you would call "Good" are good because you feel good when you focus upon them, and then more good, just naturally, follows. The things you would call "Bad" are actually good, because when you give your attention to them, a clearer awareness of what you would rather have is focused within you. Your desire for the good is born within you, right then. And, in the moment that that desire is born—the good begins to come to you. Because, in your newly focused desire, there is asking that is always answered. You just have to figure out how to let it in. That's the key, right there: To allow it, or to let it in.

Sara smiled as she listened to Solomon. There was nothing she loved more than to hear Solomon explaining how things work. He had told her that words do not teach, that it is life experience that teaches, and that the very best of all is when you are able to put the two together. Sara loved it when Solomon's words explained to her what her life experience was showing her. She remembered Solomon telling her that you never know more clearly what you **do** want than when you are living something that you **don't** want. But Sara loved Solomon's different way of explaining it to Annette: *When a new desire is born within you, it is always answered. You just have to figure out how to let it in.*

I like to call this, The Art of Allowing, **Solomon** continued. *The Art of Letting it In.*

"Letting what in?" Annette asked.

Letting in all that you consider to be good: Clarity, Life Force, Well-being, Health, Balance, Focus, Abundance, Seth, back in the tree house...

"So, you're saying that it is a good thing that a bad thing happens, like Seth being banished, because it makes us want what we had, in the first place, even more?

Exactly!

"Well, wouldn't it have just been better if he had never been banished, to begin with?"

Well, it may seem so, but not really, because this new contrast causes you to define, more clearly than ever before, what you desire. And without the contrast you would miss all of the fun of focusing it back into place. And, you would miss the motion forward into an even better place.

Annette did not look convinced. "I don't know, Solomon..."

You see, girls, the best part of your wonderful physical life experience is figuring out new things that you desire. You are like pioneers, out here on the leading edge of thought. You get to decide the direction that you would like to go—and then, all kinds of Universal Forces assist you in making it happen.

Sara smiled as she listened. She remembered Solomon explaining all of this to her, before, and he had called those Universal Forces, the "Fairies of the Universe."

Solomon looked at Sara. *You might call them the Fairies of the Universe.*

Sara giggled. She loved it when Solomon read her mind.

"I still don't get it," Annette whined. "It just seems to me that..."

As a result, of what has happened here, Solomon asked, *if you were speaking directly to the Fairies of the Universe, what would you tell them that you would like them to do?*

"We want Seth to be able to come back to the tree house!" Annette whined.

Good, Solomon replied.

"But, Solomon, isn't that just putting us right back where we were, in the first place, I mean...

You are right about that, Annette. So now, I will ask you, is there anything more you might ask for?

"We want Seth's body to heal." Sara added.

"Yes, but, Solomon," Annette protested again, "we're still just right back to where we were, before. Like, what's the point of getting hurt, so that you can heal, or getting banished, so that you can get unbanished. I don't get it!"

Sara frowned. Annette was making a good point.

Well, girls, why don't you think about it for a while. The first step is to see if you can discover any new desire that goes beyond just getting you right back to where you were before: What do you now want, more than ever before? And, meanwhile, I think I'll ponder all of this from a broader view. And with that, Solomon lifted, with his powerful wings, and flew away.

The girls sat looking at each other.

"Thanks a lot, Solomon, you're a big help," Annette teased.

"Yeah," Sara said, smiling.

"What do we NOW want?" Annette repeated Solomon's words.

"I want Seth to come back!" Sara began.

"I want him to be all healed," Annette added.

"And no scars." Sara said. "And I want his parents to leave him alone and let him do what he wants."

"Yeah," Annette added. "I want adults to stop treating us like children. I mean, we know a lot more than they give us credit for."

"Yeah," Sara added. "And to trust us more."

"And to listen to our ideas more."

"To not boss us around so much."

"To let us be free!"

Sara and Annette sat looking at each other.

"Well, I guess we did get clearer about what we want. I mean, I guess I've thought of all of those things before, but never so clearly as now," Annette said.

"I know," Sara said. "That was neat."

Solomon glided in from across the river and swooped down onto the platform next to the girls.

Well, girls, from the rockets I witnessed shooting out of this tree house, I'd say your desires have reached a bright new level. I'd say you have done an excellent job of Step One.

Sara and Annette smiled.

And now, girls, let's work on Step Three.

"Step three?" Annette said. "What happened to Step Two?"

Step Two is not your work, Annette. Step Two is the work of the Fairies of the Universe. Here's how it works: Step One is: You ask. Step Two is: The Fairies of the Universe answer. And

Step Three is: You must be in the receiving mode of what you are asking for.

You see, girls, the wonderful contrast of your time and place causes desires to bubble up within you. And once a desire is born, even if you don't speak it with your words, the Fairies of the Universe hear it, and immediately go to work on answering your desire.

"Solomon, do they always answer?"

Yes, Annette. Without exception.

"Solomon, that doesn't seem right. I mean, there are lots of things that lots of people are asking for that they aren't getting."

Well, Annette, if that is true, it can only be for one reason. They must not be in the receiving mode of what they are asking for.

Sometimes it takes a little work to begin to let it in. But it is usually not as difficult as you believe that it will be. Keep reaching for a thought that feels good, until you find one. And then, reach for a thought that feels even better. Eventually, you'll be in the place of letting it in.

"But, Solomon, what if we try and try, and just can't find one?"

Then swing from your rope, and think about other things. The most important thing is to let it in; so if you can't feel good about one subject, then choose another subject that is easier.

And remember, until you are certain you are in the place of letting it in—don't try to make anything happen with your action. Have fun with this, Solomon said. Then he suddenly lifted from the platform and flew away.

"I guess we could swing," Annette said, softly.

"I guess," Sara replied, quietly.

Neither of them really liked the idea of swinging happily through the trees when Seth was not there to enjoy it with them.

"I guess moping around won't help Seth."

"Yeah, I guess. You wanna go first?" Sara said, untying the rope and handing it to Annette.

"Okay," Annette said, putting her foot in the loop at the bottom of the rope. She held the rope with her hands and stepped off the platform and soared silently out across the river. She didn't hang upside down. She just swung quietly back and forth, back and forth. Sara watched from the platform, and wondered why Annette didn't perform her usual tricks.

Then, Annette excitedly pulled her foot from the loop and jumped onto the riverbank. "Sara, Sara!" Annette called from down below. "I have an idea! Do you want to learn how to fly upside-down?"

Sara felt a surge of enthusiasm move through her. "Yeah!" She replied, enthusiastically.

"Okay, but you'll have to come down here."

"Down there?" Sara felt disappointed. "I want to fly from up here."

"I know, and you will, but you have to start down here."

Sara climbed down the ladder. Annette was rolling up her pant legs.

"What are you doing?" Sara asked.

"We'll have to wade out into the river. Sara, I learned to hang on the rope in a gymnasium. You have to practice just hanging, first, to get comfortable with the rope, before you can jump out of a tree and hang upside-down. You have to learn the basics, first, Sara, and then you can fly from the tree."

"Oh," Sara was disappointed, but she was sure that Annette was right. "Annette, I don't think it's a good idea to wade out into the river. Some places out there are a lot deeper than you think, and the current is stronger than it looks."

Annette looked out into the river. " I guess you're right, Sara."

Sara liked it that Annette had trusted her opinion about the river, but now what would they do?

"So now what?" Annette whined. "It's too dangerous to hang upside-down, up there, and it's too dangerous to hang upside-down, down here."

"Well, we know what we *don't* want," Annette said, slowly, as if she were trying to replay what she had just learned from Solomon. "We don't want you to break your neck on your first rope trick, and we don't want to wash downstream in the river. What we *do* want," she said, loudly, "is another rope. Sara, do you know of any other rope hanging around here, anywhere?"

Sara squinted her eyes trying to think . "Yes," Sara said, happily. "There's a rope hanging in my back yard. It has an old tire hanging on it, but we could take that off."

"Let's go," Annette said, happily. "Let's go see your rope."

The girls gathered their things and nearly ran all the way to Sara's back yard. "Well, here it is," Sara said, out of breath, as she dropped her things on the grass and right away began to tug on the knot which tied the tire. "What do you think? You think we can get this tire off?"

"Oh, Sara, don't bother with that. This rope isn't big enough, anyway. The rope has to be much bigger than this for you to hang on it. This won't do. We'll have to find another."

Sara felt such disappointment. She was ready to begin hanging upside-down, right now!

"I guess we could ask the gym teacher if we could hang a rope up in the gym at school. I think that's where Seth got the ropes he used in the tree house."

"Yeah, right," Annette said, sarcastically. "And about a year from now, after your parents have filled out, like, a thousand permission forms, and the school has purchased the proper insurance and nets, and hired professional spotters, you'd have your first fun time on the rope."

"Well, it sure is easy to figure out what won't work and what we don't want. I guess we should try what Solomon was talking about. I guess we should talk about our new desire."

"We want a rope, and we want it now!" Annette said, laughing.

"We want a great big rope," Sara added, playfully.

"We want a great big, silky, smooth rope," Annette added.

"We want it to be hanging from a tree or..."

"Or from a bridge..."

"Or from the sky...."

The girls laughed.

"Yeah, that's it. We need a giant hook in the sky," Annette said.

"A giant hook!" Sara exclaimed. I know where there is a giant hook. I know where there is a giant hook with a giant rope hanging from it. It's in the barn. It's in the Wilsenholm's barn. I remember, now! I saw it when I was getting the ladder to save Mrs. Wilsenholm's kitten!"

"Where is this barn, Sara? Let's go!"

"This is great fun," Sara said. "I mean, we're doing just what Solomon said: First, we figured out what we *didn't* want, like me falling from the rope and breaking my neck or washing downstream, which helped us to know more clearly what we *did* want. And the more we thought about it, the clearer it got, until we even figured out where the perfect rope is to practice on. Now, all we have to do is make sure we're letting it in."

"Well, it feels like we're letting it in, doesn't it? I mean, I thought it was pretty amazing that you remembered the rope in the barn."

"But when I think about going to the Wilsenholm's barn without asking, that feels really uncomfortable. And when I think about asking if we can go there, that feels uncomfortable, too."

"So now what?"

"I think we might be taking action too soon. And it's getting sort of late. Let's meet at the tree house, tomorrow. We'll ask Solomon."

"Okay, see ya tomorrow."

CHAPTER TWENTY ONE

Sara had been thinking, all night, about the rope hanging in the Wilsenholm barn, and she could hardly wait to begin hanging upside-down on it. At first, the only idea that really thrilled her was that of flying through the air, hanging upside-down, with her arms stretched out in front of her, like she had seen Annette do, but Sara had left those thoughts behind, and now she was fixated on the idea of getting into the Wilsenholm's barn and learning all the tricks that Annette was ready to teach her, and "learning the basics," as Annette had said.

The next day, after school, Sara and Annette went to the tree house, and almost as soon as the girls sat down on the platform, Solomon glided down to join them. *Well, hello, my little chickadees. I see a fresh, clear desire has been hatched.*

Sara and Annette laughed.

"Oh, Solomon, are we glad to see you!" Annette began. "We have hatched a new desire, but now, we don't know how to make it happen."

Well, that's not really your job, Annette. In fact, it seems to me that you have already completed your most important work: You have given birth to the new desire.

"But, Solomon, we haven't done anything! There is still so much that needs to be done before…"

Well, Annette, I agree that there is much more that will unfold here, but the most important thing has already happened. You have given birth to a clearly focused desire. Now, all you have to do is allow it.

"Solomon, you make that all sound so easy. 'Just allow it, just let it in'—but shouldn't we DO something?"

Once your desire has been hatched, then the most important thing that you could do is to allow your desire. And you know you are allowing your desire whenever thinking about it feels good to you. And, of course, you can also allow something by not thinking about it, at all. Actually, the only time you are not allowing good things to come to you, is when you are feeling bad.

If I were standing in your physical shoes, I would DO anything I could think of that makes me feel good when I'm doing it.

"So, you wouldn't be running all over town trying to find a rope to hang from?"

Well, I might be doing that, if that were a fun thing to do. But if it wasn't fun, I'd be doing something else. I've noticed that once your desire has been launched, if you are happy, the pieces just seem to fall into place. You practically trip right over them. The path continually unfolds before you. I seem to remember, Sara has witnessed that a time or two.

When Sara heard her name she jumped a little. As Solomon had been talking, she had been deep in thought about the seemingly miraculous things that had happened to her and to Seth. So many happy endings, to what seemed like impossible situations, had resulted from them looking for things to feel good about—and not trying so hard to make things happen. But those had been much bigger problems than just trying to find a rope to hang upside-down on.

"Solomon," Sara said, "does this all work better if it really matters a lot?"

Actually, Sara, it always works, whether your desire is big or small. But I have noticed that when your desire is greater, you do tend to work harder on feeling good. And the better you feel, the faster it works—because the better you feel, the more you are allowing your desire to be answered.

Thinking about what you want—and why you want it— is usually a good tool to get you in that place of allowing, quickly.

Annette spoke very slowly, carefully choosing every word: "We want to find a strong, thick hanging rope—BECAUSE I want to show Sara how to safely hang upside-down."

Very good, Annette, Solomon said, smiling.

"And I want to find a strong, thick, secure hanging rope—BECAUSE I want to learn to hang upside-down, BECAUSE I want to fly on the rope like Annette does," Sara added, enthusiastically.

"And BECAUSE there are so many really fun things to do on the rope, that I haven't done in a long time," Annette added.

Sara added. "And BECAUSE I want to learn to do all of *those* fun things, and, BECAUSE I want to fly on the rope when Seth comes back,"

Sara and Annette beamed, almost breathless from their little rampage of enthusiasm.

Solomon smiled. *Well, girls, you certainly have been practicing the Art of Allowing, here. And did you notice how good it felt, just to THINK about what you want, and that you didn't actually have to be DOING it right now, in order to feel good?*

"Yeah, Solomon, it was pretty much fun. And DOING it, will REALLY be fun."

It surely WILL be fun, Sara. I surely do agree. And it is BEING fun. And now, I believe I will go enjoy the evening sky. I have enjoyed our chat, my fine featherless fiends.

"Did he say, fiends?" Annette laughed, as Solomon lifted into the sky.

"Yes, he did," Sara laughed. "He's so funny."

Sara and Annette each took a turn on the rope. Sara went first, and landed perfectly on the riverbank below, and then she stood back up against the tree to watch Annette's flight, watching closely every detail of Annette's perfect technique. For a moment, she felt a little impatience rising within her. She could hardly wait for her turn at flying upside-down. *Oh, oh,* she thought, *I'm not letting it in.* She could feel that this feeling of impatience didn't feel very good. "Well, it won't be long before I'm flying like that!" Sara said, right out loud—and the uncomfortable feeling softened. "Look at how beautiful she is," Sara said. "She is so nice to be willing to teach all of this to me." With those words, the uncomfortable feeling went away, altogether. Sara felt wonderful!

Annette did her usual perfect dismount, and then the girls gathered their things, and wound their way down the path. It was really not very far from the tree house back to the paved street, but the path took all kinds of interesting turns, and it always felt like a fun adventure. They happily walked and chatted their way along, knowing every log to jump over, and every bush to duck under, along this densely wooded and very shaded path.

They popped out of the shadows onto the roadway, both squinting as their eyes adjusted to the bright light.

"Watch out!" Annette shouted, as both girls came to a screeching halt, barely avoiding a collision with someone crouching down on the roadway, right at the entrance to their path.

"Mrs. Wilsenholm!" Sara shouted. "Are you all right?"

"Oh, yes, Sara," Mrs. Wilsenholm laughed. "I'm all right. It's such a beautiful day, so I decided to walk to the market. But I always buy more than I plan to, and the bottom just fell right out of my bag. Oh, dear, I seem to be scattered all over the place."

Sara and Annette gathered the scattered cans and bottles, and oranges. It was no wonder the flimsy bag had broken.

"We can use our book bags," Sara offered. "If we put some of your things in each bag, there should be enough room for all of this."

"That's a great idea," Annette agreed.

Mrs. Wilsenholm watched Sara and Annette carefully stash her scattered groceries into their book bags.

"Well, you girls have certainly saved me, today. Sara, it seems that you come to my rescue rather regularly. I don't believe I have met your friend."

"Oh, I'm sorry." Sara said. "Mrs. Wilsenholm, this is my friend, Annette. Annette, this is Mrs. Wilsenholm."

Annette smiled, politely, and looked at Sara. Both girls managed to outwardly appear poised and polite, while inwardly they were turning cartwheels. Solomon had just told them that the pieces to the puzzle would just show up—that sometimes you seem to just trip right over them—but this was too much!

The girls hiked the book bags up onto their backs, and the three of them walked down the country road together. Sara smiled as she thought about what an odd threesome they would appear to anyone passing by, but no one did pass by.

"Your bags are wonderful," Mrs. Wilsenholm said. "What a good invention. We didn't have anything like that when I was a girl, but then, we didn't tote a cartload of books home, either. My, my, your bags must be very heavy, though. I'm so sorry to have troubled you."

"Oh, no, Ma'am, they aren't too heavy. These backpacks are made to carry heavy things. We're glad to help you."

"What a beautiful place this is," Annette said, as Mrs. Wilsenholm opened the gate, and the odd threesome made their way down the entry path. "This is so beautiful!" Annette said, again. "It's like a park. This is SO beautiful." Annette didn't realize how much she had been missing the well-tended lawns and flower gardens of her former life in the city. The people in Sara's little mountain town were rather practical in their approach to life. Most managed to keep the weeds down, by occasionally mowing or turning goats or horses loose to graze, but a manicured lawn was a rare thing. And, for the most part, the only flowers, there, were wild flowers that grew randomly, with no care given by anyone. Annette's eyes passed over Mrs. Wilsenholm's lovely grounds, eagerly devouring every detail. She felt as if she just couldn't take it all in fast enough.

Mrs. Wilsenholm beamed. She took great pride in her gardens and lawns, and it felt wonderful to feel Annette's genuine appreciation for them. "Well, I'm glad you like my gardens, Annette. Most folks around here don't seem to care much about them. But then, I guess I didn't really plant them for anybody else, anyway, did I now? Leave your bags on the porch, here, and come and walk with me. I'll give you the grand tour."

Sara smiled to herself. *Annette and Mrs. Wilsenholm are certainly hitting it off well,* she thought.

"Come around to the back, girls. I'll show you my lily pond and my herb garden."

Hmmm, Sara thought. *I didn't know she had a lily pond, or an herb garden.* Sara felt a little pang of sadness move through her as she realized she had not taken any great interest in Mrs. Wilsenholm's beautiful gardens. As she watched how happy Annette's interest was making Mrs. Wilsenholm, Sara wished she had been more aware.

Annette walked and listened and pointed, and exclaimed at one beautiful thing after another. Sara followed along, feeling little or no interest in the plants, and such, but enjoying, very much, how much the two of them were enjoying all of it.

"What's going in over there?" Annette asked, pointing off in the distance toward the back of the property. "Well, I've finally convinced my husband to put in a swimming pool," Mrs. Wilsenholm said. "I've wanted one for years. There's just nothing as good for a body as to relax and move in the water. Gravity takes its toll on tired old bones, you know? Well, I guess you don't know. But it does. In the water, you are nearly weightless. You know, I was quite a swimmer when I was your age."

"Did you compete?" Annette asked, eagerly?

"Oh, my, yes," Mrs. Wilsenholm answered.

"I love that. Do you have trophies?"

"I do. Quite a few, actually. I'm not sure just where they are, these days. But I have a trunk load of them, some-where. Last time I saw that trunk, it was in the barn loft. Are you a competitive swimmer, Annette?"

"No, Ma'am, not swimming. Acrobatics. I've done it since I was little. But I'd love to compete in swimming!"

The barn! Sara shouted in her mind. *Where is the barn?* While Annette and Mrs. Wilsenholm were politely chatting on and on about swimming, Sara was feeling sudden panic, as she realized the barn was gone.

"Mrs. Wilsenholm!" Sara blurted. "What happened to the barn?"

"Oh, that old thing. Mr. Wilsenholm had it torn down, Sara. That's where the swimming pool is going in."

Sara and Annette looked at each other. They both felt as if a big door had just banged shut before them.

"Oh," Sara said softly.

"Well, I guess we should go," Annette said. "Thank you so much for the tour, Mrs. Wilsenholm. Everything is very beautiful. I've loved seeing it all."

"Well, you come back, anytime, Annette. You too, Sara. You are most welcome in my gardens."

"Thank you," Annette replied.

Sara smiled and nodded. She was so overwhelmed with disappointment, she didn't say anything. The girls walked down the path and out the big front gates.

"Well, I guess that's that," Sara said.

"See ya at the tree house tomorrow?" Annette asked.

"Yeah, see ya."

CHAPTER TWENTY TWO

Sara sat quietly in the tree house, waiting for Annette, and for Solomon. She knew Seth was not coming. It felt awful to Sara that she had adjusted to not expecting him. She never wanted to adjust to Seth's absence. *Boy, am I in a bad mood,* Sara thought.

"Are you up there?" Sara heard Annette's voice from down below.

"Yeah, come on up." Sara replied.

Annette climbed the ladder, and stretched out on the floor across from Sara. Neither girl spoke.

Sara laid on her back with her head next to Annette's. "Well, Annette, you look about as ornery as I feel."

"I only hope I don't look as ornery as *I* feel," Annette said, laughing as she said it. "Sara, what's wrong with us? This isn't like us?"

"Well, I think we were so sure that we had figured out where we were going to get a rope to practice on... It was like, everything was cooperating with us. Just like Solomon says. And then, it was like, "Oh, Mrs. Wilsenholm, may we use the big rope hanging in your barn to learn acrobatics on? *No, you may not girls. And just to make sure that you understand that you may not, I'm going to have the whole barn knocked down!*"

Both girls began to laugh.

Solomon glided down onto the tree house floor. *Hello, girls!*

Both girls sat up. "Hi, Solomon." "Hi, Solomon."

It is important to realize that things are never working against you. All things are working for you, at all times.

"It did seem like things were working for us, at first. I mean, it was amazing that we would run into Mrs. Wilsenholm right after I remembered the rope in her barn. But then..."

Things are always unfolding for your benefit, girls—if you will allow it. Everything that you are asking for is always being answered. There are only three parts to this wonderful equation of creation: One; ask. Two; the Universe always answers. Three; you must be in the receiving mode. You must be a vibrational match to what you are asking for, or you cannot let it in.

You see, girls, when you decide, from the evidence you have collected, that things are not working out for you—in that very moment, you are no longer letting it in.

"But, Solomon, the whole darn barn was gone!" Sara blurted, and then she laughed. Annette laughed, too.

Solomon smiled. *And if that barn were the only avenue through which your Well-being could flow, you may have reason to be upset, Sara. But since there are endless avenues through which your Well-being flows—being upset about the barn door closing, only keeps all other doors closed, as well.*

Not only does the Universe have the ability to answer anything that you desire, but everything that you desire is always being factored in. Just remember that any time you are feeling negative emotion, you are, in that moment, not letting it in. You are not in the receiving mode. And, do you know, your not being in the receiving mode is the only thing that ever keeps you from anything you desire?

"Wow!" Annette exclaimed. "That's big!"

Yes it is, Annette. It can be of value to pay attention to those wonderful signals that negative emotion offers. In other words, when you feel negative emotion, just stop and softly say to yourself, "I'm doing it now. Right now, I'm doing that thing that I sometimes do that keeps me from receiving the things that I desire." Then laugh, and reach for thoughts that put you more in the receiving mode.

"So, Solomon, you're saying that unless we do that thing we do that holds us out of the receiving mode, then everything that we desire will then happen?"

Yes, indeed. Annette. You ask; the Universe answers—and all you have to do is let it in.

"That seems easy enough."

"Yip," Sara replied. They felt so much better.

"So, Sara, let's make a pact with each other that we'll be extra aware of letting it in. I want to always be in the receiving mode."

"Me, too."

"We need to tell Seth, too. I really miss him."

"Yeah, me, too."

The girls looked at each other. They had just stepped out of the receiving mode—and they both knew it.

"I'm doing it now," Sara said.

"That was fast!" Annette said. "Almost as fast as we decided to always be in the receiving mode, we were *out* of the receiving mode. And now, I'm doing it again."

"This is hard." Sara laughed. "I'm doing it, now!"

The girls looked at each other. "Solomon, you make it sound simple to be in the receiving mode." Annette said, "But it is not that easy to do."

"We're doing it now." Both girls said at the same time.

"Well, the good news is, we can tell when we're not in the receiving mode. That's something. And if we can feel when we're *not* in the receiving mode, we'll be able to tell when we click back into it." Sara said.

"There must be all kinds of things we talk about that keep us in the receiving mode. And when we *are* in the receiving mode, everything we want can come."

It's wonderful, when you think about it, girls: Good things—all the good things that you could ever want—are making their way into your lives. And all you have to do is let them in.

"I'm good with that." Annette said.

"Yeah, me too." Sara said.

Be playful about it. Solomon advised. *It will be great fun for you to be aware of when you are in the receiving mode. It's fun to observe others, too. It is really rather easy to tell if someone is in the receiving mode or not. Well, I'm off. I'll be seeing you.*

Annette and Sara watched Solomon lift off the tree house floor, and fly high into the sky. "Do you think Solomon always sees us?" Annette asked, softly.

"Yes. I think he does."

"Doesn't that bother you? I mean, if he sees everything...?"

"Well, at first, I was bothered. But after a while, I realized that Solomon loves me. His feelings for me do not seem to change no matter what I'm doing or how I'm feeling. And so, now, instead of worrying about what he might think of me, I just feel good because I know he loves me. He loves you, too, you know."

Annette smiled. "Yes, I know."

CHAPTER TWENTY THREE

Nearly a month passed, and Sara and Annette did their best to pay attention to the way they were feeling. Both girls were getting very good at staying in the receiving mode.

"Sara, I heard that your cat got run over, yesterday," Annette, teased Sara.

"Oh, well, it is probably for the best," Sara answered, in fun. "I've heard that flat cats are very popular now."

"I also noticed that Pete's Drug Store burned down last night."

"Oh, well, that is probably for the best," Sara answered. "I've been eating far too many candy bars, anyway."

"I heard your little brother ran away from home."

"Then, it's true! The Universe is answering my every desire." Sara replied. "My world is now complete."

Annette laughed. "Seriously, Sara, we are getting pretty good at this, don't you think?"

Sara had to agree. With far less trouble than she would have ever believed, she had discovered that it was really quite easy to find thoughts that feel good. Especially since so much depends on feeling good.

When Sara found herself missing Seth, she would quickly turn her thoughts to remembering an especially fun time, or imagining one in the future. When she caught herself worrying about Seth's wounds not healing well, or about his parents forbidding him to come to the tree house, she would try to remember that all good things are coming. And, that since Sara and Seth and Annette were all asking, and since the Universe is answering, that it was only a matter of time before they would all be back in the tree house together again.

"Let's play a game," Annette said, enthusiastically.

"Okay." Sara agreed, having no idea what kind of game Annette was thinking about.

Annette laughed. "Oh, Sara, I do love you. You are such a good friend. You're up for anything, aren't you?"

Sara smiled. She could tell, by Annette's enthusiasm, that she knew she had a good idea. And Sara trusted Annette; Sara could not imagine Annette suggesting anything that would not feel good. "What game?"

"The eavesdrop game."

"The what?"

"Eavesdrop game."

"I've never heard of that one," Sara laughed. "Did you just make it up?"

"Yes," Annette grinned. "But, listen, don't you think it would be fun? We'll go around town, you know, pretending to be minding our own business, but we won't be. We'll be listening in on what people are saying."

Sara looked at Annette. Sara had worked rather hard, especially lately, at minding her own business. This seemed like a pretty weird game.

"We'll call it the 'Receiving Mode Game'. We'll just listen in and see if we think people are in the receiving mode of what they want, or not."

Sara brightened. Now she understood what Annette was talking about. "So, it isn't really like sticking our noses into other people's business. It's more like gathering evidence of receiving?"

"Right! Where do you think we should go?" Annette asked.

"Pete's Drugstore is a good place to start. There are always people at the soda fountain talking to Pete. And we can stand behind the magazine rack, and they won't even know we're there." Sara and Annette climbed down the ladder from the tree house. "This is going to be great fun," Sara said.

The bells on the drug store door clanked as the door banged shut behind them, causing both girls to jump a little, as if they had been caught sneaking in.

"Hello, kids!" Pete said, as he continued to put more candy bars on the rack near the cash register. "What can I do for you, today?"

"Oh, nothing, not yet, anyway," Sara said quickly. "We just want to look around."

"At the comic books," Annette added, quickly. "We want to look at the comic books."

"Well, you know where they are," Pete said, as he opened another box of candy bars, paying very little attention to the girls.

Sara and Annette ducked behind the magazine rack. "Why do I feel so sneaky?" Sara whispered to Annette.

Annette laughed, and covered her mouth with her hand. "Because, you are."

Both girls laughed.

"There's nobody in here," Sara said. "I don't think I've ever seen this place so empty."

The bells on the door clanked again, as three ladies entered.

"Let's get a booth," one of them said.

The booths were at the back of the Drug Store stretched out along one wall. Sara and Annette peered from behind the magazine rack. "Sit there! Sit there!" Sara whispered under her breath, hoping that they would sit close enough that she and Annette could hear them.

Sure enough, a large woman squeezed into the first booth.

"Yes!" Sara said, triumphantly.

"Shush!" Annette reminded her. "We're under cover here."

"My back is killing me," the large lady said. "I don't know what I've done to it. Doc says he can't find any reason for it to hurt so much. The x-rays don't show a thing."

Sara saw Annette take a notebook from her pocket. She wrote, "#1, focuses on what she doesn't want."

"Well, it will probably be better before you know it," a bright voice offered. "Sometimes these things just go as quickly as they came."

Annette wrote, "#2, tries to influence #1 back into the receiving mode."

"Not likely," the large woman said. "Can't remember when my back didn't hurt. I guess I'm just going to have to get used to it. Pain medicine doesn't work, either. To tell you the truth, I don't think my doctor knows what in the heck he's doing."

Annette wrote, "#1 doesn't seem to want to get into the receiving mode." Sara laughed, as she read, and covered her mouth with her hand.

The waitress stopped by the table to take the order. Sara and Annette looked at each other. They were pleased to get such good evidence, already.

After the waitress left the table, Sara and Annette heard someone else begin speaking. "Elizabeth, did you tell Emily about your surprise?"

Sara saw Annette write: "# 3 changes subject. Feels better."

"Not yet. But I was about to," the bright voice said, happily. "I got the job. I'm moving to the city!"

"The city?" The first woman said. "Aren't you afraid to move to the city all alone?"

"Afraid? Of what?" The bright voice said, a little less bright, now.

"Well, you know how dangerous it is to live in the city. Don't you watch the news? Terrible things happen in the city. Oh, I'm worried about you. I hope you'll be all right."

"Oh, don't worry," Liz said. "I'll be fine." But she didn't sound fine. In fact, she sounded like a completely different person than she had been only a few minutes ago.

Sara read, as Annette wrote: "#1 wins. #2 now out of receiving mode."

"Liz is always fine," the third woman said. "Liz, you always do great, no matter where you are or what you are doing. Has anything bad ever happened to you? No." She answered her own question. "It hasn't. Not ever! Liz, you lead a charmed life, and there is no reason for that to ever change. You have a wonderful opportunity here. And you deserve it. I'm so happy for you, and I just know you are going to have a wonderful time. I'm so proud of you!"

Sara and Annette looked at each other. "Wow! What a blast of the receiving mode that was." The girls were so amazed with this barrage of positive words that, for a moment, they forgot they were hiding. Both girls stood up to try get a look at whoever was spewing such wonderful words.

"Find what you're looking for, girls?" Pete shouted from behind the soda fountain.

"Yes," Sara said, "I mean, no, not really." The girls scampered out of the drug store.

"Let's wait here, Sara."

"For what?"

"Don't you want to get a closer look at them? To see if we can tell who said what?"

"Oh, yeah, I do." Sara answered.

The girls sat on the bench in front of the town's only bank, and waited for the three ladies to finish their meal. Then the bells on the door of the drug store clanked again as the three women came back out onto the street. They stood in front of the drug store, for a few minutes, exchanging a few more words that Sara and Annette could not hear, and then they went their separate ways.

Then, one of them turned and walked toward Sara and Annette. She was a slender, happy looking woman, wearing a pretty, bright flowered dress with a pretty purse slung over her shoulder. She walked, or rather floated, down the street, and as she passed Sara and Annette, she said to them, "Well, girls, have you ever seen a prettier day?"

"No, Ma'am," Sara and Annette said at the same time.

"Me, too," the woman said. "Aren't we the lucky ones?"

"We sure are," Annette said.

Sara watched as Annette made another notation in her book. "#3, still in receiving mode. Wants to pass it on to others."

"Oh, dammit," Sara and Annette heard a disgruntled voice coming from a car across the street. They were not surprised to see the large lady from the drug store. She was standing next to a car, with the door open. Her sleeve seemed to be caught on the door latch, and she was tugging at it, awkwardly. "Well, now I've torn my dress. That's just great."

Sara and Annette giggled softly to each other. Annette wrote in her book. "Things aren't getting better for #1, yet. Still, not in receiving mode."

"Look out!" someone shouted. Sara and Annette looked up to see an empty grocery cart rolling across the parking lot, headed right for Number One's car. She sat frozen behind the steering wheel, helpless to do anything about it. She covered her face with her hands, crying, "Oh, no, my husband will kill me."

As soon as Sara realized what was happening, she had started to run toward the cart, and she intercepted the grocery cart just before it reached the woman's car. The woman sat tensed, waiting for the inevitable crash, and when it didn't come, she uncovered her face to find Sara smiling in her car window.

"Hi," Sara said, softly. "This cart almost got you."

"Hey, lady, I guess it's your lucky day," someone, who had witnessed the whole thing, called to her from the sidewalk.

"I don't think so." The woman said sarcastically, "I don't *have* any of those."

"Any of what?" Sara asked, thinking that the woman was talking to her.

"Any lucky days." My cousin (I just had lunch with her) talks about how lucky she is all the time. Oh, she's just full of lucky days. But not me. I don't have lucky days."

"Well," Sara said, timidly. "How about a lucky moment? Maybe you could just start there."

As the woman looked at Sara's sweet face, she felt her own tension lift, and she broke into a gentle smile. "You know, Sweetie, you may be right. Thanks to you, I certainly did have a lucky moment."

"Well, you have a good day, now," the woman said, as she turned the key to start her engine. A song blared from her radio. "Well, what do you know," the woman said, looking at Sara. "That's my favorite song."

"Hey," Sara laughed. "Two lucky moments in a row. I think you're on a roll."

The woman laughed. "Well, perhaps you're right. Let's keep our fingers crossed."

Sara crossed her fingers on both hands and held them up for the woman to see.

The woman laughed.

"I'm Sara," Sara said, holding out her hand, as her mother had taught her, and shaking the woman's hand.

"I'm Emily," the woman said. "In fact, I have a card. Well, it's really my husband's card, but I've written my name on it, too."

Sara took the pretty card and nearly dropped it as she read it: "#1 in Home Repair".

Oh, Annette, you're not gonna believe this! Sara thought to herself.

CHAPTER TWENTY FOUR

Annette had let Sara know that she would not be coming to the tree house for a few days, as her family was going to the city to visit her aunt, so Sara took her time walking home from school. She decided to stop at Pete's drug store to get a candy bar.

Sara paid for her candy bar, and as she opened the door of the drug store to leave, Mrs. Wilsenholm walked in.

"Oh, hello, Sara," Mrs. Wilsenholm said. "I'm so glad to run into you."

Sara laughed, thinking about the last time they ran into each other, when she and Annette nearly ran right over Mrs. Wilsenholm on the path. Mrs. Wilsenholm knew exactly what Sara was laughing about, and she laughed, too. "These are a little better circumstances, now, aren't they, Honey?"

"Yes," Sara said, still smiling.

"Sara, I couldn't help but notice that you didn't seem to be very happy about my new swimming pool. I want you to know that you and your nice friends are more than welcome to swim in it, as soon as it is completed. Everyone in town won't be coming by, you understand? But I like you and that sweet girl. Annette? Is that right? And, of course, your friend, Seth. The three of you are most welcome. Unless you don't want to come, of course. You do like to swim, don't you, Sara?"

"Oh, yes, Maam. That's very nice of you. I am happy that you are building a swimming pool. I think it will be very nice for you. I just..." Sara's voice trailed off.

"What, Dear?"

"I was just so surprised that the barn was gone."

"Oh, that dilapidated old thing. That barn was as old as the hills. Nearly as old as me."

Sara laughed. Mrs. Wilsenholm was really a very funny lady.

"Sara, come in and sit with me, and have a soda. I hate to sit alone. What would you like?" Mrs. Wilsenholm headed for a table at the back of the drug store, not waiting for an answer from Sara, but just assuming that Sara would follow right along.

Sara followed Mrs. Wilsenholm, and they slipped into a big booth at the rear of the drug store. Mrs. Wilsenholm ordered a root beer float. "Old Pete still makes the best float in the world," Mrs. Wilsenholm said. "Would you like a float, Sara?"

"Yes, please," Sara smiled. It was hard to pass by on anything reported to be the best in the world.

"Now, Sara, tell me, what was it about my old barn that was so important to you?"

Mrs. Wilsenholm was beginning to feel like an old friend. It felt nice to have an adult be so completely interested in Sara's interests.

"Well," Sara began. "Annette can swing..." Sara stopped right in the middle of her sentence. Suddenly, it didn't seem so wise to tell the owner of the trees, that they were swinging from, that one of them was hanging by her knees and hanging upside-down over the river. What if this information made Mrs. Wilsenholm feel guarded? What if all of them were banished from the tree house?

"Go on, Sara. What is it that your friend, Annette, does?"

"Well," Sara stalled, trying to decide how to approach this delicate subject." Annette is a gymnast. She's really very good at it. She can... She said she would teach me some of the tricks she can do, but first we needed to find a large sturdy rope. And I remembered seeing one in your barn. We thought we would ask you if we could practice there, sometime, but, then, the barn isn't there anymore. So, I guess that's that."

"Well, now, Sara, that seems like a rather simple problem to solve. We don't need a barn to hang a rope in, now, do we? Not with all of these trees around here. I'll tell you what, Honey, I'll ask Mr. Wilsenholm what became of that big old rope, and we'll just find a place to hang it. I'll bet your friend, Seth, could find a place for you over by your tree house."

Sara jumped as Mrs. Wilsenholm spoke. It felt strange to have anyone except Sara and Annette, and Seth, talking about the tree house. The waitress brought the root beer floats. Sara immediately began sipping on her straw, trying to hide her uneasiness about Mrs. Wilsenholm's casual mention of the tree house.

"I walk there quite often," Mrs. Wilsenholm continued. Sara could hardly believe what she was hearing. Mrs. Wilsenholm goes to their private tree house?

Mrs. Wilsenholm noticed Sara's uneasiness. "I usually go there while you kids are in school. There's a large, flat rock, at the river's edge, that I particularly enjoy. It's a good place to sit and be still. There's nothing like the feel of water moving by to lift one's spirits. I never go there when I think you and your friends might be there, Sara. I know how important it is to have a private place to be."

Sara took a deep breath, and then sucked on her straw again.

"Isn't that a good root beer float?"

"Yes, it is," Sara answered. "Thank you, so much, for inviting me."

"I saw a very big owl in the tree house, last week, Sara." Mrs. Wilsenholm said, carefully studying Sara's reaction as she spoke. "Have you seen it?"

Sara choked, as she drank. She put her napkin over her face, as she tried to compose herself. She could not believe what she was hearing.

"It's really a beautiful thing. It flew out across the river and then right up into your tree house, and then it swooped right down to the river, right past where I was sitting. It was as if it was looking me over. And then, it flew right back up into your tree house. Have you ever seen it, Sara?"

"Oh, yeah," Sara said; trying to sound calm and not very interested, "I've seen it around."

"Hmmm."

Sara held her breath.

"That's what I love about the country, Sara. There are so many beautiful birds and animals that live all around us. They're wary of us humans, and well they should be. But it's nice how we all get along. I like to think that this world is big enough for all of us. I like sharing my trees with you and your friends, Sara, and with that owl, too."

Sara sighed a sigh of relief. *That felt too close,* she thought. And then she thought, *I sure do like this lady.*

Sara sucked the last drop of her delicious root beer float from the bottom of her glass, making a very loud slurping sound. Mrs. Wilsenholm did the same thing, at the same time. They both laughed.

"I'll ask Mr. Wilsenholm about the rope, tonight, Sara. We'll figure out how to get it up in the tree, once we find the rope."

Sara wanted to find the words to somehow tell Mrs. Wilsenholm that she really didn't want anyone going to the tree house to hang the rope. But, how could Sara tell Mrs. Wilsenholm that someone wasn't welcome on her own property?

"On, second thought," Mrs. Wilsenholm added, "maybe it's better if nobody else goes over there. No point in everyone in town knowing about your secret place."

Sara felt relief. And then surprise. Mrs. Wilsenholm seemed to be reading her mind.

"Well, we'll figure something out, Sara. I'll let you know, once we find the rope."

"Okay, thanks," Sara said. "And thank you for the best root beer float in the world."

"You're welcome, Honey. I'll see you later."

CHAPTER TWENTY FIVE

"Solomon, did you know that Mrs. Wilsenholm knows about you?"

Why does that surprise you so, Sara?

"Because, Solomon, you are supposed to be a secret. I thought that only Seth, and now Annette, were the only ones who knew about you, besides me."

Mrs. Wilsenholm must have been about your age, Sara, when we first met.

"What!? You knew her when she was a girl?"

Her name is Madeline, you know. Everyone called her Maddie back then. She was quite a tomboy, Sara. These trees weren't quite as big back then, as they are now, but, still, she spent a great deal of time in the top branches of these old trees. Her father owned the sawmill and lumber yard, and before he died, he left it to Mrs. Wilsenholm and her husband.

"Solomon, how did Mrs. Wilsenholm, I mean, Maddie, how did she meet you?"

I think it would be a good idea if you ask Maddie to tell you about that.

Sara felt disappointed. She really wanted to hear more about how Solomon had known Mrs. Wilsenholm when she was a young girl. Sara had felt reluctant to admit to Mrs. Wilsenholm her own relationship with Solomon. Solomon had been such a well-guarded secret for so long, it felt wrong to begin speaking openly about him to anyone else.

I'll talk to you later, Sweet Girl, Solomon said, stretching his wings, getting ready to fly away.

"Solomon, wait," Sara said, quickly.

Solomon folded his wings back against his body, and looked lovingly at Sara.

"Solomon, how many other people in town know about you?"

Oh, I suppose there have been quite a few, over the years, Sara. But most of them no longer remember our encounter. Some of them never recognized me, at all; others knew me and then, in time, forgot all about me.

"I'll never forget you, Solomon!" Sara cried out. "How could anyone ever…"

Maddie is one of those rare ones, like you, Sara, with whom I have an eternal connection. She has an eternal connection to you, too. Have a wonderful evening, Sara.

Solomon flew up into the sky and out of view.

Sara sat on the floor of the tree house. Her head was spinning with all of this new information. She couldn't decide what to do next, or even how to feel. She wanted to find Seth and tell him everything that she had learned; this felt like such big information; too big to keep all to herself.

I have an eternal connection to Mrs. Wilsenholm? Sara thought. *That's weird. I wonder what Solomon meant? Is that why Mrs. Wilsenholm keeps showing up, just at the right time to help us?*

"Sara! I'm so glad you're still here. I thought maybe I would miss you!"

"Seth! Seth! Am I glad to see you! What in the world are you doing here? I thought you weren't supposed to be here! Won't you get in trouble? Oh, Seth, I've missed you! I have so much to tell you!"

Sara looked at Seth. It was so good to see him.

"Seth, you're all better. I can't even see where your cuts were. Seth, you didn't get any scars!"

"Nah," Seth answered, nonchalantly. "I never get scars."

Sara smiled. There was so much to talk about.

"When I got home from school, today," Seth continued, "my mother said that my dad had called and said that I should meet him and Mr. Wilsenholm over at the stables, to do some sort of chore for them. So I went to the stables, and my dad gave me a gigantic rope, and said that I was to take it to Mrs. Wilsenholm. My dad said that he had offered to take it to her in the ranch pick-up, but that Mr. Wilsenholm made a very specific point that Mrs. Wilsenholm wanted *me* to bring it to her. So, my dad said, "She's the boss. It's not my job to question her." So he told me to take her the rope and do whatever she wanted me to do with it. Something about how she had a project for me, that might take a few weeks after school, if I was willing. And then my dad looked me right in the eye, and said, 'And you are willing, aren't you, Son?'"

Sara began to laugh. In fact, she couldn't stop laughing.

Seth grinned, enjoying Sara's uncontrollable laughter. "Sara, Sara, what's so funny? Tell me, Sara, what's so funny?"

"Oh, boy, do I have a lot to tell you," Sara said, still laughing, but trying to stop. "She's one of us, Seth."

"Who is? What do you mean?"

"Maddie. Mrs. Wilsenholm. She's one of us. She knows about Solomon, Seth. She's known about Solomon since she was our age."

"Sara, what in the world?" Seth just couldn't imagine what Sara was going on about.

"Seth, think about it. Think about how Mrs. Wilsenholm keeps popping up in our lives at just the right moment; remember how she saved our tree house and the trees?"

"Yes," Seth said, hesitantly.

"And remember how it was *her* idea that your Dad be the ranch foreman?"

Seth nodded. "Yes, that's right."

"And now, look at this. Not only did she manage to make it so you are allowed back in the tree house. She got your father to *order* you here. Oh, Seth, she is just the most amazing woman. And she's one of us, Seth! She knows about Solomon."

"Sara, how do you *know* all of this?"

"I keep bumping into her, literally. It seems like everywhere I go, she's there. And she invited me to have a root beer float with her, and she told me that she comes to the tree house, really often, but not when us kids are here, because she knows we like our privacy. And that she has been coming to this place in the woods, for years. And she said that she saw a big owl in our tree house—and she asked me if I had ever seen it."

"Solomon?! She saw Solomon?" Seth asked.

"Yes, and when I told Solomon that she had seen him, he didn't blink an eye. He just calmly said, 'Oh, yes, Maddie and I have been friends for years.' He said lots of people in this town knew about him when they were kids, like us, but most of them don't remember. But Mrs. Wilsenholm still remembers."

"Sara! Seth! I am so glad you are here!" Annette shouted, breathlessly, as she climbed up the ladder to the tree house.

"Annette, you're back! This is so great! Did you have a good time? Oh, Annette, you're not going to believe what's happened."

"Tell me. What's going on? Seth, what are *you* doing here? Aren't you going to get in trouble? Look at you. You're all better. Seth, you look so good."

Seth began to laugh. The girls were both talking so fast. It felt so nice for all three be back together again. "Not only will I not be in trouble," Seth spoke, slowly and deliberately. "I have, in fact, been *ordered* to be here."

Sara nodded. "Oh, boy, Annette, do we have a lot to tell you!"

"Sara, you got the rope!" Annette said, excitedly.

"How'd you know?" Sara asked.

"Because I saw it in the wheel barrow, down there!"

Annette said, leaning over the edge of the railing and pointing down below.

Sara and Annette stood, leaning against the railing, looking down at the long awaited rope—and beamed at each other. "We did it!" they both said, at the same time.

"Yeah, what's with this *rope,* anyway?" Seth asked.

"Where to start?" Sara said, shaking her head.

"It was Solomon's idea," Annette chimed in.

"Well, yeah, sort of," Sara said. "We were in the tree house right after you got banished, and we were really missing you. We weren't having any fun without you here. And when we asked Solomon what to do, he said (you know what he always says) to find a thought that feels better. But we couldn't find anything about your not being here that felt good. Even when we tried to think happy thoughts about you, it just reminded us that you weren't here. So, Solomon said we should think about something else. So, we took turns swinging from the rope. And then, Annette got the idea that she could teach me how to fly upside-down. And then, she said that we needed to find a big thick rope so that I could practice hanging upside-down, before I jumped out of the tree to try it. And then, we sort of forgot about how sad we were that you weren't here. And then it became our mission to find a big rope..."

Sara's voice trailed off. She began to laugh.

Annette was laughing, too.

"What's so funny?" Seth asked.

"Solomon is such a clever bird." Sara said.

Solomon swooped down from high up in the tree.
Well, now, I see the gang's all here.

"Solomon, it worked!"

"What worked?" Seth could not figure out what they were all talking about.

Of course it worked, Sara. It always works.

"What always works?" Seth still didn't understand.

Everything, always works, Solomon smiled. *Anything and everything that you ever could want always works out—if you'll only let it.*

Sara and Annette sat, smiling and listening.

"It sure is easier to hear you say those words, today, Solomon, than last month, when Seth was banished from this place." Annette said.

Solomon smiled.

"Solomon, did you know, all along, how this would all turn out?"

You will never be in a place where it has "all turned out", because it is always in the process of becoming more.

"But you know what I mean. Did you know that Mrs. Wilsenholm was going to make it so that Seth could come back to the tree house?"

Well, Sara, I didn't spend anytime trying to figure out HOW it would come about. But I did know that it WOULD come about, because I know that whatever you ask for is always answered. You see, whenever you ask for anything, it is always given. It's your job to let it in.

"The Art of Allowing," Sara added, smiling.

That's right, Sara. There are three steps to achieving anything that you desire. Step One is: to ask for it. Step Two is: the answering. And Step Three is: you have to let it in.

"Sounds simple enough," Seth said. "So, what's the catch?"

The catch? Solomon asked.

"Yeah. It can't be that simple, Solomon. I've asked for lots of things that I didn't get. There are people all over the place who want things, and are asking for them, that aren't getting them. So, what's the catch?"

Solomon smiled. *Well, Seth, the "catch" is that when you are asking for something that you do not have, you are usually so aware that you don't have it, that everything about you is pulsing and oozing the feeling of not having it. And when you are radiating signals about not having something—you can't let it in.*

You have to be radiating a signal that matches your own desire, before you can let your own desire in.

Sara and Annette's eyes flashed bright with new understanding. "Yeah, Seth, like, we wanted you to come back to the tree house, in the worst way." Annette said.

Sara laughed. "In the worst way," sure did emphasize what Solomon had just said about oozing signals that are the opposite of your own desire.

"We tried and tried to think happy thoughts about your being back in the tree house, but every time we tried, we just missed you more. So Solomon suggested that we find something else to think about." Annette explained to Seth.

"Yeah, so Annette got the idea that she could teach me how to swing upside-down on the rope. And that really sounded fun to me. And don't take this the wrong way, Seth, but we sort of got so excited about getting a big rope and hanging it up, someplace, that we sort of forgot how much we missed you."

"Yeah, and then, finding the rope, didn't turn out to be all that easy, so we had to really think about *that,* and then, other things to think about just kept showing up. It isn't that you weren't important, Seth. We just got a little distracted for a while."

Solomon interrupted. *The most important thing to understand is that once you have asked, all kinds of things come into place to give you what you have asked for. You don't have to continue to ask, again and again. It is best when you realize that once you have taken Step One, (the asking) that your work is to jump right to Step Three. (the allowing)*

"But, what about Step Two?" Seth asked.

Step Two is not your work.

"Well, whose work is Step Two?" Seth asked.

That is the work of Law of Attraction, Creative Life Force, God Force, The Fairies of the Universe. All manner of unseen forces of Well-being converge to accommodate you in whatever you are asking for.

Sara and Seth, and Annette, sat quietly. Solomon's words felt so wonderful, so comforting—and so sure.

Step Three, Solomon continued, *is what you are always working on. Putting yourself in the place of letting in what you have been asking for.*

"And we do that by?" Seth still wanted more explanation from Solomon.

By not doing that thing that you do that doesn't let it in.

Sara and Annette began to laugh. Seth laughed, too.

"That thing we do? What thing? Solomon, what do you mean?"

Well, actually, it is quite a few things. But you always know whenever you are doing it, because you are feeling negative emotion at the same time that you are doing it. You see, kids, whenever you are feeling any negative emotion, like fear or anger, or blame, you are, in that moment, focused on the exact opposite of something you want. So you cannot be in the mode of allowing what you DO *want if you are oozing the vibration of what you* DON'T *want.*

"So," Sara said, excitedly, "when we were sad, because, Seth couldn't come to the tree house, we were doing that thing. But when we got interested in something else that didn't make us feel bad, then we weren't doing that thing, so…"

"We could let in what we *did* want," Annette finished Sara's sentence.

Well, kids, I think you've got it, **Solomon said.** *It would require many hours of concentration just to be aware of how many remarkable things have come into place and how many intentions, that you have launched, over the past few weeks, have come into being.*

It seems like magic to some, like miracles to others, like good luck or good fortune to others, but what always has happened is, somehow, consciously or unconsciously, deliberately or indeliberately— YOU HAVE TO LET IT IN!

"Think about it, Sara," Annette said, excitedly, "almost as soon as we started looking for the rope, amazing things began to happen." .

Well, actually, kids, amazing things begin to happen the moment that you launch your desire. They begin even while you are right in the middle of your dilemma or problem, or disaster. But you cannot see the evidence of all of this help that is lining up for you, until you stop doing that thing you do—and let it in.

"Hmmmm," Sara pondered, leaning back against the tree. They all sat there feeling wonderful.

"We're such lucky ducks," Annette said. "Well, I don't mean lucky, I mean…"

Feeling lucky, is a good way to feel, Annette. Feeling lucky is certainly a match to letting in what you desire. Whether you are feeling lucky or blessed or appreciation, or just plain happy—you are letting in all that you consider to be good.

But, when you feel unlucky or sad or overwhelmed or angry or blameful, or guilty, or any of those bad feeling emotions—in that moment, you are not in the receiving mode.

Yes, "lucky" is a very good way to feel. I don't know about ducks, however. Solomon smiled. *Well, kids, I'm off. I'll leave you here to count your blessings.*

"Bye, Solomon, we'll see you tomorrow!"

I'm such a lucky owl, Solomon said, as he lifted from the platform.

All three kids burst into laughter.

You're right, Annette, **Solomon called back,** *it just does-n't have the right ring to it. Let's see, what rhymes with owl. Howling owl. Not quite right. Allow. Allowing owl! I am an allowing owl, I am an allowing owl, I am an allowing owl. Much better! I think I like it!*

CHAPTER TWENTY SIX

Sara sat in the tree house waiting for Seth and Annette to join her. She leaned, lazily, back against the tree, looking out across the river, and just plain felt good. She breathed deeply and stretched her arms up over her head, and felt little shivers of pleasure move all the way up her spine. "I feel so great!" she called out from her perch. "I wish everybody in the world could feel as good as this, if only for a moment. They would never want to go back to feeling less."

It felt to Sara almost as if she were in a state of suspended animation. The earlier events of the day felt like long ago, almost as if they had happened to someone else, and she felt no impatience about the day continuing to unfold. Annette and Seth seemed to be taking longer than usual arriving at the tree house, but Sara felt not one bit of anxiety, or impatience. This moment, in time, felt perfect. Nothing that she should be doing that she wasn't doing, nothing that she wanted to do that she wasn't doing, nothing missing, nothing needed—everything just right.

"Now, this is how it's supposed to feel," Sara said, right out loud.

You are right, Sara, Solomon said, as he landed on the platform next to Sara. *The way you feel right now, that's the way life is supposed to feel, in every moment. Perfect and expanding. Enough, but becoming more. Satisfied, but eager for something else. Complete—but never, ever finished.*

Sara felt rapturous love pulsing through her as she looked upon her wonderful feathered friend. "Oh, Solomon, it feels so good to feel so good. Whatever has come over me?" Sara laughed, as those words came out.

Who you are has come over you, Sara. Or perhaps it is better to say, you are now allowing who you really are to be. This is your normal state of being. This is who everyone would be—if they could just let it be.

"I know you are right, Solomon and I do want to just let it be. I think everyone would want to let it be, if they knew how good it feels, and if they knew how to do it. Why don't we always feel this way, Solomon? Why does it seem so hard to just let it be?"

Pretend that you are a beautiful gem, aquamarine, like the beautiful blue ocean. Little by little, from exposure to the elements of your environment, a light coating of dust and hard water mutes the beauty of that which you are. And because of the unnatural coating, you don't see out as clearly as you once did, and others cannot see you as clearly, either. But with a little bit of work, you can easily remove the unnatural accumulation of sediment, and you can then shine as brightly as you ever did—and feel as wonderful as you ever did.

As you sit in this clear, good-feeling place, it is easy to understand this. Much easier than when you are sitting in an uncomfortable place. But, just for a moment, imagine sitting here with a variety of thoughts moving through your mind: You are a young girl, sitting in her tree house, waiting for friends. But instead of being light hearted and clear, as you are today, imagine that you are weighted down by many things, sort of like the sediment on the gem. In other words, your favorite teacher is leaving the school, and you feel bad about that. You saw boys fighting in the parking lot, and you worry that it may escalate into something really serious, like things you have seen on television. You heard your father complaining about his boss, last night, after dinner, and you realized that he is not having a very good time at work, lately. You heard that your friend's mother is very sick, and you feel bad for her, and even a little bit vulnerable, yourself. Can you feel how, with each unwanted situation that you ponder, your joy is muted just a bit more?

Now, make a decision, "I may think about my teacher leaving, later, but, for now I think I'll remember my favorite thing about him. I may wish for things to be different with the boys fighting in the parking lot, but, for now, I think I'll just mind my own business and assume they are working things out in their own way; I wish them well. I want my father to be happy at work, but all of that is really up to him, and I'm sure he doesn't need my help in figuring this out. He always figures things out. I want my friend's mother to be well, but my worry helps not one bit. I think I'll leave that to the work of her family, or the doctors, or the angels, or to her Solomon."

If any worrisome thoughts remain, just say, "I don't really have to think about that, now. Maybe later, but not right now." Try to imagine releasing each worrisome thought, one after the other. Another, another, and another. And, with each release, you feel a little lighter, a little brighter, a little happier, until, eventually, without exception—you allow yourself to be the bright, clear, happy person that you naturally are.

Everything that makes your life less than happy is because you are, whether you realize it or not, holding onto something that mutes the happiness. If you are angry; if you could just let it go, you would feel immediate joy. If you are sad; if you could just let it go, you would feel immediate happiness. If you have a headache; if you could just let it go—you would feel immediately wonderful. Any time you feel anything less than very, very good, it is because you have picked up some worrisome thought and you are continuing to carry it with you. You can stop, right now—and put it down.

Sara smiled. Everything that Solomon was saying made so much sense to her. And, in her clear, good feeling moment, she wondered why anyone would ever carry anything around that didn't feel good.

Well, Sweet Girl, I'll talk to you later. Have a wonderful afternoon!

Solomon seemed to be as light as air as he lifted, almost silently, from the platform and flew off into the distance. Sara smiled as she watched the ease with which Solomon moved through the sky. "That's just how I feel," she said, out loud. "I love you, Solomon."

CHAPTER TWENTY SEVEN

"Sara, are you up there?" Sara heard Seth's voice from down below.

"Yes, I'm here. I'm up here!" Sara shouted, leaning over the tree house railing and catching a glimpse of Seth coming down the trail toward the tree house.

Hmm, something's up, Sara thought to herself. She could hear, in Seth's voice, that something was going on, and she tensed a little bit, not sure that she even wanted to know what it was.

She tried to collect her thoughts and hold herself steadily in the good-feeling place that she and Solomon had shared, only moments before, but she could feel her light, happy feeling diminishing.

"Sara, I think something sort of bad might be happening, and I don't want you to be upset."

"About what?"

"Well, there's a big crane up on the Main Street bridge."

Sara had no idea what Seth was talking about. She couldn't imagine why Seth thought that that would upset her.

"Sara, I think they're straightening up your leaning posts. I think they're putting a new chain link fence across the bridge."

"Oh," Sara said.

Sara's mood had changed so swiftly, she almost felt dizzy. Leaving her coat and her books right where they were, Sara scampered down the ladder.

"Sara, I don't think that's a good idea. They've got everything all blocked off."

"I gotta go," Sara called back. "Coming?"

Seth had seen that determined look on Sara's face before, and he knew there was no use in trying to stop her. "Yeah, I'm coming," he said, as he scampered down the tree. Sara was running fast, and Seth had to really run to keep up with her.

There were many workers standing on the bridge, and bright orange cones had been placed across the roadway to prevent any cars from passing. The giant crane was sitting right in the middle of the bridge, and Mr. Thompson, the town sheriff, was directing traffic.

"Hey, you kids can't cross here, today. You have to go around the block. I don't want you getting run over, or causing any trouble."

Sara stopped short. She wanted to shout back at him. "You're the one making the trouble here, not me."

"Oh, man," Sara whined, "why can't they just leave things alone?"

Sara felt awful. In fact, she couldn't remember the last time she felt this bad. In fact, this felt especially bad, after only a few minutes ago she had been feeling so good. But it was not easy to feel good when something really really important to you is being destroyed.

"Come on, Sara, let's go to the tree house. Let's talk to Solomon. Maybe he can help." Sara followed Seth back to the tree house. Her body felt so heavy she could barely drag herself down the trail. Her emotions ranged from feeling so angry she wanted to knock the sheriff right into the river with her own two hands, to feeling absolutely powerless to do anything about it, at all. And, she felt embarrassed, mad at herself that in only a few short minutes she had gone from feeling the best she could ever remember feeling, in her whole life, to feeling as bad as she could ever remember feeling.

Well, hello, my fine, featherless friends, Solomon said, in a chipper voice, as he landed on the platform. *A little sediment has clouded your clear view, Sara?*

Seth looked puzzled. He had no idea what Solomon was talking about.

Why don't you explain to Seth what I mean, Sara?

Sara did not look up. About the last thing that Sara felt like doing was to explain to Seth about clear, bright aquamarine gems.

Solomon sat, quietly, waiting for Sara to begin. Seth was quiet, too.

Sara scowled. She could not find the beginning place.

Well, Sara, maybe a good way to begin would be to tell Seth how the whole gem story came about. Tell him how you were feeling, and then tell him about our gem conversation.

"Well," Sara began, slowly. "I got here early today, and so, I sat here all alone for a while. And the longer I sat here, the better I felt. It was like, I didn't have a care in the world, and everything in my world felt just perfect. I felt so good. I felt like standing up and shouting it right out loud. I almost did. And then I wished that everybody could feel like that. I wished that I could always feel like that."

"And then Solomon told me that we would all feel like that if we weren't finding all kinds of not good feeling things to think about. He said that we are all like beautiful clear gems. Clear and bright, and beautiful, but that, over time, as we find things that we don't like, things that we worry about, that it's like, we get covered, little by little, with sediment. But, that anytime we want, we can polish off the sediment and go back to that clear good-feeling place."

Sara looked at Solomon. "That's just how it happens, isn't it, Solomon? Something happens. Something that we can't do anything about. And we watch it happen. And it makes us feel bad. And sediment gets on us, and changes us. That's why, as people get older, they are less happy, isn't it? They get all covered up with sediment."

That is how it happens, Sara. Little by little, people find things to worry about, and they feel less and less joyful as they find more and more things to worry about. But you know, Sara, it doesn't have to be that way. You don't have to let the sediment pile up on you, muting your clarity and your joy. If you polish your gem a little every day, you'll remain bright and clear, and anyone can polish themselves off, anytime they want to by reaching for thoughts that feel better. You don't have to think thoughts that make you feel bad, Sara. There are plenty of other thoughts to choose from.

"I know, Solomon, but I just think it's rotten that they are ruining my leaning perch."

Well, Sara, you can think that thought, you are certainly justified in thinking it, because there is truth to it: It is your leaning perch. And you have adored having it. And they are removing it. All of that is true. But the question I want you to ask yourself, is, how do I feel when I think it? And if the answer is, I don't feel good, then choose another thought, and accumulate no sediment.

"Like what?"

You could think about how you have this wonderful tree house that really is so much more than the leaning perch was. You could think about how you can come here whenever you want to. Think about the swinging rope, or your friends, Seth and Annette, or about me, Sara, your dear, adorable, dead (turns out not so dead) allowing owl friend.

Sara laughed. So did Seth.

Think about how the river still flows, and how the sun still shines, and the rain still falls, and the food still grows, and the moon still rises, and how the tree house still stands. And think of all of the millions of other wonderful things that, if you had time to think about them, would make you feel good, because they are just the way you like them. And then, that uncomfortable feeling will just lift right up off of you, leaving you bright and clear, and naturally good-feeling. That's who you are, Sara. Nothing else will ever do for you.

And, in time, you will come to the place where nothing matters more than that you feel good. Looking at facts, or pointing out truths, will become far less important than finding thoughts that feel good.

Sara was quiet. She felt better, that was certain, but there was something that was still troubling her. Solomon had helped Sara and Seth feel better about many things, and in each case, once they began to feel better, things seemed to turn around, and the problem was fixed. She remembered when Mr. Wilsenholm was going to cut down the big trees where the tree house is, and how Sara and Seth really worked on getting into a better feeling place—and then, how everything changed and the trees were not cut down. They were even given permission to play in the trees. She remembered how Seth's father was planning to move Seth's family out of town, and how Sara and Seth focused their clear thoughts, from a good feeling place, and then, how miraculous things happened that allowed the family to remain in Sara's mountain town. The list went on and on. Finally, Sara's question was clear:

"But, Solomon. You always help us to feel better, and then things change for us. You've helped us fix so many things. How come we can't fix this?"

Solomon smiled. *Sara, I have not been teaching you to fix things. What I have been teaching you is how to put yourself in a position, in a vibrational position, to allow your natural Well-being to come to you.*

"But, Solomon, they are going to destroy my leaning perch. My favorite place. They're going to ruin it."

Sara, how would you feel if several other kids from your town discovered your leaning perch and wanted to go there every day?

Sara scowled. "I wouldn't like that."

But what if they really like it? What if your leaning perch became their favorite place to be, also?

"Oh, I get it, Solomon, you think I should be willing to share. I know, I should be willing, but..."

Would you try to organize it so that you could all have your turn? Would you pass rules that say you have to be a certain age, or a certain size to lie in the leaning perch?

Sara continued to scowl. "Solomon. I don't get what you mean? That all sounds like way too much trouble. I'd probably just go somewhere else, but..."

Sara, you are absolutely right. It would be too much trouble to try to organize everything in a way that would please everyone. I don't think you could do it if you tried for a hundred years. But something that you can do, that really isn't very hard at all, is—you can take your attention away from whatever it is that is bothering you, and put your attention upon something that feels good. It does require some effort, especially in the beginning, but, in time, you get very good at turning your attention toward things that feel good. And before you know it, you do feel good.

"But, Solomon, I still won't have my leaning perch."

But, Sara, isn't the reason you want it, only so that you could feel good?

"Yes."

And if you DO feel good—well, isn't that just as good?

Sara was quiet. She could see that Solomon had a point. "But, Solomon, I thought you were teaching us how to get things to turn out the way we want them."

I am teaching you that, Sara. But getting things the way you want them is not about fighting others who want things differently. Getting things the way you want them is about finding thoughts that feel good so that you then allow, or let in, what you do want.

Things always work out for the best. That is the way it is supposed to be. But, if you are fighting against something that you do not want, you aren't allowing things to work out well for you.

"So, you're saying that if I find thoughts that feel good, they won't destroy my leaning perch?"

I'm saying that if you find thoughts that feel good—you'll feel good—and your learning perch will be a non-issue.

"But, Solomon, I don't want my leaning perch to be a non-issue." Sara felt agitated.

Solomon smiled. *What about making your happiness your main issue? Your only issue?* "Nothing is more important than that I feel good."

"And what will happen to my leaning perch?"

Whatever it is, won't matter to you.

"Why not?"

Because, you'll be happy, anyway.

Sara began to laugh. She could see that she was not going to get anywhere with Solomon on this one.

Sara, Solomon continued, *people often believe that things have to be a certain way before they can feel good. And then, when they discover that they don't have the power, or the votes, or the strength, to make things be the way they need them to be, then they resign themselves to unhappy, powerless lives.*

What I want you to come to understand is that all of your power is in your ability to see things in a way that keeps you feeling good. And when you are able to do that, you have the power to achieve anything that you desire.

Everything that you desire is trying to make its way to you, but you must find the way to let it in. And you cannot let in what you desire, when you do not feel good. Only in feeling good, can you let in those things that you desire.

Sara was quiet again. She was beginning to understand what Solomon meant.

You live in a big world, Sara, with many other people who may want things to be different than you want them to be. You cannot convince them all to agree with you, and you cannot coerce them to agree with you, and you cannot destroy all of those who do not agree with you. Your only path to a joyous, powerful experience is to decide, once and for all, that you intend to feel good, no matter what. And, as you practice turning your thoughts to things that do feel good—now, you have discovered the secret to life.

"Thanks, Solomon. I think I get it. For now, at least."

Anytime, Sweet Girl, anytime.

CHAPTER TWENTY EIGHT

Sara's eyes suddenly opened. It was as if something had awakened her. She laid there in the darkness, listening to see if she could hear anything, but the house was quiet. She looked at her bedside clock and saw that it was 1:11 AM. *It's way too early to get up,* Sara thought, and she pulled the blankets up over her shoulders, and fell back asleep.

Sara's eyes suddenly opened. Again, it was as if something had awakened her. She looked at her clock. 2:22 AM, the dim green lights on her bedside clock read. "Oh, well," she sighed, turning over and falling fast asleep, again.

Sara's eyes suddenly opened. She turned quickly to see what time it was. The clock said 3:33 AM. Sara smiled. "3:33, this is too weird!"

I wouldn't say it is too weird, Sara. Not too much weird, and not too little weird—just the right amount of weird. Sara heard Solomon's quiet voice whispering in the darkness.

"Where are you?" Sara whispered.

Meet us at the tree house, Sara heard Solomon's quiet voice, again.

Sara sat up in bed. She was wide awake, now, but she wasn't sure if she had been dreaming, or if she really had heard Solomon's voice. She looked at the clock. It still read 3:33. She jumped out of bed and pulled a sweat shirt and sweat pants right on over her pajamas. She put on her shoes and a coat, and quietly opened her bedroom window. The moonlight was very bright. And as her eyes adjusted to the darkness, she had no trouble finding her way to the tree house. "Just the right amount of weird." Sara laughed to herself. "I'm not sure everyone would agree with that."

As Sara approached the tree house, she could hear voices. It was Seth's voice, and Annette's voice. *What in the world?* Sara thought.

"Seth, Annette, what are you doing here?" Sara called, as she climbed up into the tree house.

"Sara, it was the weirdest thing. I woke up at 1:11 and then at 2:22..."

"And then at 3:33," Sara finished Annette's sentence.

"Me too," Seth chimed in, "me too." This is really weird! And we both thought we heard Solomon's voice telling us to meet at the tree house."

"This is soooooo weird!" Annette said, shivering as she spoke.

"Just the right amount of weird," Sara laughed.

Just the perfect amount of weird, Solomon said, as he plopped down on the platform with the three of them.

"Solomon!" they all said, at once, in excited anticipation of what was about to happen. "Why are we all here?"

Well, we're not quite ALL here. We'll wait for Maddie. We've been flying together on every full moon, for many years, now. It was her idea to invite you all to join us.

"Maddie flies?" Sara blurted. She could barely believe her ears. "But she's a grown up!"

"Who is Maddie?" Annette and Seth said at the same time.

"Maddie, you know Mrs. Wilsenholm. Her name is Madeline, but they used to call her Maddie, when she was our age." Sara explained.

Age has nothing to do with flying, Sara. Flying is about how light you feel. You cannot be weighted down with problems and worries, and still fly. It is your pure spirit that soars, Sara.

I know it seems to you that you have all joined me here in your beautiful bodies, but your bodies are actually still soundly sleeping in your beds. Tonight, I will fly with the truest part of who you are. And we will have a wonderful time together.

"You mean, we're not really here with you?"

Oh, yes, you are really here with me. But your bodies are still fast asleep in your beds.

"But, Solomon, I have flown with you, before. My body flew with you, before."

You flew with me, Sara, but your beautiful body was tucked, snug and warm, in your bed.

"But, Solomon, I remember, I flew with you."

YOU did fly with me, Sara. And tomorrow, you'll most likely remember tonight's flight. When you are light, and free from worry, and in a happy place, allowing who you really are to be— you'll remember.

"Are we really going to fly, Solomon?" Annette blurted. She just couldn't stand it, anymore. "I don't care if my body comes or not, Sara, I just want to fly. How do we do this? Come on, let's get going."

"What is that?" Seth said, pointing out across the river.

A large, white form seemed to be floating right toward them.

"It's Mrs. Wilsenholm!" Sara blurted. "Maddie, Maddie, it's you. You're flying!"

"Well, I guess I am, Sara. And it's a beautiful night for it, too. Would you like to join me?" Maddie said, reaching out to take Sara's hand. And without even thinking about it, Sara stepped off of the platform and floated right over to take Mrs. Wilsenholm's hand.   Sara reached back for Annette, and Annette reached back for Seth—and they all floated out over the river.

"Yahoo!" Seth's voice echoed down the river.

"Can you guys believe what's happening here?" Annette called. "Can you believe this?" She repeated. "This is unbelievable!"

Sara laughed.   She remembered that feeling of amazement.   Almost more than you can contain.   And even now, she was feeling it, again.

"Sara, why don't you show Seth and Annette what you remember about flying," Mrs. Wilsenholm said.

Sara said, "Well, I don't remember there being much to it.   All you have to do is decide where you want to go, and you just, sort of, go there.   If you want to go up, look up.   If you want to go down, stretch your toe downward, sort of pointing it in the direction of where you want to go, and down you go."

"Try it," Mrs. Wilsenholm said, smiling.

"Up!" Seth shouted, and up he zoomed. "Up, a little more," he said, more softly, and up, a bit more, he floated.

"I wish to go over there," Annette said, dramatically pointing across the river—and across the river she went.

"Me too," Sara said, and across the river she went.

"I want to go up, now down, now up, now down!" Seth shouted, enthusiastically, and up and down and up and down, and up and down he went! He could not stop laughing. "Boy, that's a ride and a half," he called to the girls.

"You want to fly to the school?" Annette asked.

"I do," Seth agreed.

"Me, too," Sara agreed.

And off they went. Mrs. Wilsenholm followed along behind.

They floated up over the football field, waiting for Mrs. Wilsenholm to catch up with them.

"Have you noticed, kids," Mrs. Wilsenholm explained, "that whatever you decide, causes an immediate response?"

"Yes, this is so great!" Annette answered.

"Did you notice that words are not required. Only a clear intent from you?"

"Yeah," Seth answered. "It's like, whatever we want, just happens."

"Join hands, and I'll show you something quite interesting."

Sara reached out and took Seth's and Annette's hands, and they reached out and took Mrs. Wilsenholm's hands, forming a circle.

"Now, Sara, you decide to go up, and, Annette, you decide to go down, and, Seth, you decide to go sideways. On three: one, two, three!"

"Nothing happened! Why didn't anything happen?"

"Now, let go of everyone's hands. Now, Sara, you decide to go up, and, Annette, you decide to go down, and, Seth, you decide to go sideways.

"Ohhh!" they all exclaimed as Sara blasted up and Annette blasted down, and Seth blasted sideways.

Everyone laughed. Eventually, they gathered back together in their floating circle.

"You see, kids, when you are floating, singularly, and you are clear about what you want, your own intentions are immediately acted on, because you are in complete agreement with you. But when we were all joined as a group, and intending different things, nothing happened."

"Now, join hands again, and now, let's intend to go upward."

Seth and Sara, and Annette projected that intention—and up they rose.

"Wow!" Sara said. "This is cool."

"When we weren't in agreement, why didn't we just all pull in opposite directions, Maddie?" Sara asked. "I mean, why didn't we each get what we wanted and just tug at each other?"

"Well, that could happen. With some people it does happen that way. But you are such good friends. I suppose your intention to get along with each other is so strong, that rather than tugging at each other, you waited, instead, for a group consensus."

"Hey, where's Solomon?"

I'm here, Solomon said, from the sky, high above them. *I'm enjoying your techniques. I believe you have taken flying to a place it has never been before.*

Everyone laughed. "This is so much fun. I wish we could stay here, forever," Annette said.

Flying is a wonderful thing, kids. I do it all the time. But then, I am a bird, now, aren't I. And flying is a nice thing for you to do, from time to time, also. But you have intended to do your soaring in different ways. It would not be a good thing if flying distracted you from your extremely valuable human perspective. But, I think it would be all right if you stayed here for a few more minutes. There's someone else who would like to fly with you for a while.

"Someone else?" Sara was surprised. "Who else around here knows about you, Solomon?"

She's not exactly from around here, Sara. But she does know all of us very well.

Solomon turned and gazed across the football field. A beautiful, white, dim form floated toward them.

"Mom, Mom! Oh, Mom, it's you!" Annette squealed, flying toward the approaching form.

Sara and Seth, and Maddie, held back, watching Annette streak across the field and into the arms of her mother.

"Oh, Mommy, Mommy, you're here. You're here, and you are as real as real can be."

Annette's mother laughed, gently. "Well, I guess I am real, Annette. We all are. We are all always real. I am so glad that you could come here to meet me in this way."

"Mommy, are you going to come back, like Solomon did, and live with us again?"

"Oh, sweet Annette. Now, how would we go about explaining that to the neighbors? I will never really leave you, Annette. I am always just a thought away. And whenever you want me, I'll be right here. In very special times, like tonight, you'll be able to see me, and anytime you're happy—you'll be able to hear me, and sense me."

Annette smiled at her mother. She didn't know why, but, somehow, she understood, fully, everything her mother was saying to her. It all seemed perfectly logical and comfortable.

"Mommy, what's it like to be dead?"

"Well, Annette, I wouldn't really know. It turns out that there is no such thing. I am as alive as ever. More, really. And happy, oh, Annette, I didn't realize that such happiness could exist."

"I'm glad, Mommy. I'm happy, too."

"I know you are, Sweet Girl. I see it every day."

"Well, kids, we'd better get a move on. We don't want to turn into pumpkins or anything like that." Maddie said.

"Mommy, will I see you again?" Of course, Annette, we'll visit often. Have fun with your friends. And kiss everyone at home for me."

Annette's mother faded softly into the night sky, and Sara and Annette and Seth, and Maddie floated silently over the football field. Sara put one arm around Annette's neck and one around Seth's neck. Seth reached out for Maddie and Maddie reached out for Annette, and the four of them floated there, silently, over the football field.

Sara rolled over in her bed, and opened her eyes. The clock said 3:34. She smiled. "Oh boy, was that weird!"

Just the right amount of weird, she heard Solomon's voice in her head.

CHAPTER TWENTY NINE

Sara could barely stand to wait until school was out so she could meet with Seth and Annette, and talk about the unbelievable experience they had had the night before. Or, at least, Sara thought they had all had it the night before, because the more time that passed, the more Sara began to wonder if she had, maybe, only dreamed it.

She understood what Solomon had explained about how her body had remained sleeping in her bed, and that her consciousness was having those magical flying experiences, but this experience had seemed to go so far beyond anything Sara had ever experienced. It seemed just too wonderful to be true. Would Seth and Annette remember it, as Sara remembered it?

Sara could see Annette coming toward her with a group of other kids. She was dying to drag Annette aside, right there in the hallway, to ask her what, if anything, she experienced last night, but Sara knew she should not talk about any of this where anyone, who would not understand, might hear.

Sara watched Annette's pretty face as she got closer. *Does she remember?* Sara wondered. Annette looked right at Sara, as if she had heard her thoughts, and smiled a beautiful knowing smile at Sara. Annette's face was more beautiful, than ever, this morning. She looked so calm, and relaxed. She looked joyous!

"I'll see ya," Annette called back over her shoulder, looking at Sara with a clear intensity that let Sara know, without any doubt, that Annette would be at the tree house after school.

Sara hurried toward her classroom. *I wish we could just go to the tree house now,* Sara complained under her breath.

Seth came running up from behind Sara and slipped a small note paper into her hand as he rushed past her. He turned around and winked, as he hurried down the hallway.

His note read, "TREE HOUSE—TONIGHT—FOR SURE!"

He remembers. Sara smiled to herself.

The final bell rang, and Sara went directly to the tree house. She just couldn't wait to meet up with Seth and Annette so they could talk about what had happened last night.

When she arrived at the tree house, Annette was already there, and before Sara could climb the ladder up into the tree house, Seth came running into the clearing right behind her.

She giggled as she tried to climb up into the tree house, faster. It felt like Seth might just climb right over the top of her, if she didn't hurry up and get out of the way.

The three of them sat breathless on the platform, just looking at each other.

Finally, Annette spoke, first. "Did what I think happened last night, really happen?"

"I think, what you think happened, happened. But I'm not exactly sure what you think happened." Sara said, laughing between her words.

"One thing's for sure," Seth said. "I don't think we should tell anybody else what I think that you think, that you think happened."

Solomon zoomed in from across the river and plopped down on the platform beside them. *Well, hello, my fine featherless friends. Or should I say, my glorious gaggle of ghosts? What's new? Or should I say, What's up?*

Everyone laughed.

"Solomon," Sara said. "We're so glad to see you. Wasn't last night amazing?"

I don't know that I would call it amazing, Solomon said. *It all felt perfectly normal to me.*

"Yes, but Solomon, what is normal for you, is still pretty far out for the rest of us," Seth said.

Actually, Seth, the three of you are rediscovering what truly normal is.

"Normal?" Sara and Annette said, at the same time. "This is normal?"

Yes, kids, remembering your unlimited nature. That is normal.

Feeling joyous, as you move about with gay abandon.

Understanding that there is no death, and therefore never any separation between loved ones. That is normal.

Feeling alive and aware.

Being so full of who you really are, that self adoration is always present.

Knowing Well-being. That is normal.

Understanding that, no matter what, All Is Well. That is normal.

The three of them sat quietly listening to Solomon's beautiful words.

Loving your lives...

Feeling excited about what is before you...

Understanding that the joyous journey never ends...

Knowing that you can figure it all out as you go along...

Loving others who will play with you along the way...

Understanding that we are all different, and yet perfect as we are... That is normal.

Realizing that you will never, ever get it done...

And that you never get it wrong...

Feeling so full of yourselves, and so in love with who you truly are, that nothing distracts you from your joyful moments...

Now, THAT *is normal.*

But, everything else is all right, also.

The three of them laughed, again. "Oh Solomon," Annette began, "I love you so much. I am so happy. I am just so happy."

You are, indeed. Solomon smiled.

"So, Solomon, what's next?" Sara asked, excitedly, understanding that Solomon can see clearly into the near and distant future.

More, Solomon said, simply.

"More of what?" Sara asked.

More of whatever you give your attention to.

Sara laughed. "Oh, yeah. It's always that way, isn't it?"

It is, indeed, my friends. It always has been, and it always will be.

Solomon lifted from the platform and flew off into the horizon. The three friends sat watching Solomon until he was completely out of view. They looked at each other, glad for their friendship.

"So," Annette said, jumping to her feet. "Sara, are you ready to learn how to fly, up-side-down?"

Seth grinned. He knew how much Sara had been wanting to learn to do that.

Sara smiled, as she looked at her friends.

"More," she said. "I do like that."

THE BEGINNING

The Science of Deliberate C

A Quarterly Journal and Catalog Adder ̣ ̣ ̣ ̣...

Jan, Feb, Mar, 2002 — VOL 19

Lock On To
Your Receiving Mode (Page 6)

STARTER SET: ABRAHAM BASICS!
(Page 10)

Economic Business Slumps? (Page 24)

Newest Group Series — Summer, 2001 Album
(Page 12)

Y ou must be in the mode of joy, or of feeling good, in order to let in the things you've been asking for. You must first get happy. You cannot work hard enough to make the things that you want happen — it is only in your attitude of joy that they do.   Abraham — 6/23/01

Abraham-Hicks Publications
P.O. Box 690070, San Antonio, TX 78269
Tel. (830) 755-2299 or FAX (830) 755-4179
On line — www.abraham-hicks.com
© Copyright 2002

Dear Friends,

It is only slightly embarrassing that the outside temperature on our vehicle has read close to 73 degrees for months now. For years we have been traveling this nation, and we are now in our third year of driving it in our "Monster Bus", but *this year* has been absolutely amazing. We have managed to rendezvous with fabulous weather, perfect driving conditions, and gorgeous vistas, day after day. It really does feel like the entire Universe is cued up just to surprise and delight us.

Today is October 24th, 2001, and we're in Asheville, NC, on the grounds of the splendid Biltmore Estates, at the edge of the lake where we have been coming for years to work on our Sara books. There is a slight wind blowing, just enough to cause a steady falling of colored leaves, all around us. I hope we can stay here long enough that our car is completely covered. It's about 5 o'clock in the afternoon and the lake is full of Canadian geese, who, like us, have dropped in to refresh and to remember that all is truly well. I swear, each one of them looks over at us, and smiles, as they swim by.

I was just thinking that in a moment like this is it impossible to know anything other than absolute Well-being. And then I thought that maybe we should just stay here and let the leaves completely cover us up and never leave this place or this feeling. And then Abraham said to me, "Esther this glorious feeling of Well-being will travel with you wherever you go."

And then I remembered, over the last few weeks, a never ending stream of moments of Well-being that have been following us from place to place:

Big, wide, paved, open roads leading everywhere we want to go.

Other travelers nodding, smiling, waving, tooting, passing by....

Toll booth attendants joking, playing, smiling, well-wishing us along our way.

RVers, campers, tenters, back packers happily rendezvousing at the end of the day.

Grocery stores spattered across this nation, so easy to find on a moment's whim.

Restaurants full of delicious foods and efficient people caring for us.

Carefully placed and perfectly run fuel stops whenever we feel like stopping.

Couriers speeding to and fro delivering anything we could possible want as soon as tomorrow.

Marvelous hotels all over the place, fully staffed as if they exist only to please us.

Stores and shops and all manner of wonderful things at every turn.

And in every city and town, and place in between, we find willing, helpful, wonderful people enhancing our experience day after day.

I love knowing that Well-being abounds wherever we are, and that Source Energy eternally flows for all of our benefit.

Well, the geese have begun to chatter one to another. They seem to be saying, "Time to move on to another wonderful place."

The wind has subsided, and the leaves have stopped falling, and I don't think our car will be covered even if we do stay longer. And now, I have remembered that Well-being abounds wherever we are, and so, I'm ready to go now, too.

We'll see you along the trail.

AND, we do love you,

Jerry & Esther

Dear Friends,

We do love receiving your messages and reading your letters and notes that come by the thousands! Even though we can't personally respond to you, we will continue to read and listen to and relish your wonderful responses to Abraham's materials... And we will continue to expect you to be aware of how very much we appreciate your delightful addition to our delicious physical experience — and to the upliftment of All-That-Is.

From our hearts,
Jerry & Esther

90 DAY EVENT SCHEDULE DETAILS

From time to time there are changes in our scheduling, so please reserve in advance with our San Antonio office at (830) 755-2299.

PREPAID RESERVATIONS ARE REQUIRED.

4/20/02 — San Antonio, TX — Held at the Westin Riverwalk, 420 W. Market St., San Antonio, TX 78205. For directions or sleeping room reservations call (210) 224-6500. Saturday 9AM to 4:20PM. $150.00.

5/4/02 — Atlanta, GA — Held at the Renaissance Atlanta Hotel, 590 W. Peachtree St. NW, Atlanta, GA 30308. For directions or sleeping room reservations call (404) 881-6000. Saturday 9AM to 4:20PM. $150.00.

5/7/02 — Virginia Beach, VA — Held at the Norfolk Waterside Marriott, 235 E. Main Street, Norfolk, VA 23510. For directions or sleeping room reservations call (757) 627-4200. Tuesday 9AM to 4:20PM. $150.00.

5/11/02 — Silver Spring, MD — Held at the Gaithersburg Marriott Washingtonian Center, 9751 Washingtonian Blvd., Gaithersburg, MD 20878. For directions or sleeping room reservations call (301) 590-0044. Saturday 9AM to 4:20PM. $150.00.

5/13/02 — Philadelphia, PA — Held at the Philadelphia Marriott West, 111 Crawford Ave., West Conshohocken, PA 19428. For directions or sleeping room reservations call (610) 941-5600. Monday 9AM to 4:20PM. $150.00.

5/18/02 — Tarrytown, NY — Held at the Westchester Marriott Hotel, 670 White Plains Road, Tarrytown, NY 10591. (914) 631-2200. Saturday 9AM to 4:20PM. $150.00.

5/21/02 — Buffalo, NY — Held at the Buffalo Niagara Marriott, 1340 Millersport Hwy., Amherst, New York 14221. For directions or sleeping room reservations call (716) 689-6900. Tuesday 9AM to 4:20PM. $150.00.

5/25/02 — Chicago, IL — Held at the Chicago Marriott Schaumburg, 50 North Martingale Rd., Schaumburg, IL 60173. For directions or sleeping room reservations call (847) 240-0100. Saturday 9AM to 4:20PM. $150.00.

5/28/02 — Indianapolis, IN — Held at the Indianapolis Marriott, 7202 East 21st Street, Indianapolis, IN 46219. For directions or sleeping room reservations call (317) 352-1231. Tuesday 9AM to 4:20PM. $150.00.

6/1/02 — Kansas City, KS — Held at the Overland Park Marriott, 10800 Metcalf, Overland Park, KS 66210. For directions or sleeping room reservations call (913) 451-8000. Saturday 9AM to 4:20PM. $150.00.

6/15/02 — Boulder, CO — Held at the Westin Westminster, 10600 Westminister Blvd., Westminister, CO 80020. For directions or sleeping room reservations call (303) 410-5000. Saturday 9AM to 4:20PM. $150.00.

6/22/02 — Fort Collins, CO — Held at the Holiday Inn, University Park, 425 W. Prospect Avenue, Fort Collins, CO 80526. For directions or sleeping room reservations call (970) 482-2626.Saturday 9AM to 4:20PM. $150.00.

6/29/02 — Salt Lake City, UT — Held at Hilton Salt Lake City Center, 255 S.W. Temple, Salt Lake City, UT 84101. For directions or sleeping room reservations call (801) 328-2000.Saturday 9AM to 4:20PM. $150.00.

7/3/02 — Boise, ID — Held at Double Tree Hotel, Boise Riverside, 2900 Chinden Blvd., Boise, ID 83714. For directions or sleeping room reservations call (208) 343-1871. Wednesday 9AM to 4:20PM. $150.00.

7/6/02 — Seattle, WA — Held at the Embassy Suites, 3225 158th Ave., SE, Bellevue, WA 98008. For directions or sleeping room reservations call (425) 644-2500. Saturday 9AM to 4:20PM. $150.00.

7/13/02 — Portland, OR — Held at the Embassy Suites, 9000 SW Washington Square Road, Tigard, OR 97223. For directions or sleeping room reservations call (503) 644-4000. Saturday 9AM to 4:20PM. $150.00.

7/20/02 — Ashland, OR — Held at Windmill Inn of Ashland, 2525 Ashland St., Ashland, OR 97520. For directions or sleeping room reservations call (541) 482-3010. Saturday 9AM to 4:20PM. $150.00.

2002 GENERAL WORKSHOP SCHEDULE

Please reserve
in advance with our San Antonio office at (830) 755-2299.

PREPAID RESERVATIONS ARE REQUIRED.

Following is general information for up-coming workshops. Specific location and other details will be provided when you make your reservation, or you may request this information at any time.

Time Format for following events: 9AM to 4:20PM

1/5/02	Saturday	Houston, TX
1/26/02	Saturday	San Antonio, TX
2/2/02	Saturday	Tucson, AZ
2/9/02	Saturday	Los Angeles, CA
2/23/02	Saturday	San Diego, CA
3/2/02	Saturday	North Los Angeles, CA
3/9/02	Saturday	San Rafael, CA
3/16/02	Saturday	San Francisco, CA
3/23/02	Saturday	Phoenix, AZ
3/28/02	Thursday	El Paso, TX
4/20/02	Saturday	San Antonio, TX
5/4/02	Saturday	Atlanta, GA
5/7/02	Tuesday	Virginia Beach, VA
5/11/02	Saturday	Silver Spring, MD
5/13/02	Monday	Philadelphia, PA
5/18/02	Saturday	Tarrytown, NY
5/21/02	Tuesday	Buffalo, NY
5/25/02	Saturday	Chicago, IL
5/28/02	Tuesday	Indianapolis, IN
6/1/02	Saturday	Kansas City, MO
6/15/02	Saturday	Boulder, CO
6/22/02	Saturday	Fort Collins, CO
6/29/02	Saturday	Salt Lake City, UT
7/3/02	Wednesday	Boise, ID
7/6/02	Saturday	Seattle, WA
7/13/02	Saturday	Portland, OR
7/20/02	Saturday	Ashland, OR
7/27/02	Saturday	Sacramento, CA
8/3/02	Saturday	San Rafael, CA
8/10/02	Saturday	San Francisco, CA
8/17/02	Saturday	Los Angeles, CA
8/18/02	Sunday	North Los Angeles, CA
8/24/02	Saturday	San Diego, CA
8/31/02	Saturday	Sedona, AZ
9/2/02	Monday	Albuquerque, NM
9/7/02	Saturday	Chicago, IL
9/14/02	Saturday	Detroit, MI
9/21/02	Saturday	Cincinnati, OH
9/28/02	Saturday	Syracuse, NY
10/1/02	Tuesday	Albany, NY
10/5/02	Saturday	Boston, MA
10/12/02	Saturday	Tarrytown, NY
10/15/02	Tuesday	Philadelphia, PA
10/19/02	Saturday	Silver Spring, MD
10/26/02	Saturday	Asheville, NC
11/2/02	Saturday	Dallas, TX
11/23/02	Saturday	San Antonio, TX
11/30/02	Saturday	Tallahassee, FL
12/7/02	Saturday	Boca Raton, FL
12/14/02	Saturday	Orlando, FL

Lock On to Your Receiving Mode

When the new desire is born within you, and it has not yet manifested — are you still okay with that?

The contrast will continually give birth to desire within you, and if, even though it has not yet manifested, you are satisfied with where you are — while you are eagerly anticipating your inevitable expansion — then everything about your vibration would be perfect for the perfect eternal expansion that.

Your Dissatisfaction Hinders

Your most common hindrance is that feeling of dissatisfaction about something that you want, that you do not have. Either there is something that you've got that you don't want, and you're unhappy that you can't get rid of it, or there is something that you desire that has not yet come fully to you, and you are irritated or depressed that it has not yet come. *Your feeling of dissatisfaction is your biggest hindrance, and it is also the simplest one to release once you understand how it all works.*

Ask, and it is Always Given

Many of you have heard it many, times: When you ask, it is given.

Your feeling of dissatisfaction is your biggest hindrance.

Whether you are a cell in one of your magnificent bodies, or in a plant's body, or you are the fully conscious personality that you know as you, when you ask for something — and you are asking constantly whether you use words or whether your experience just helps you to conclude the desire — when you have desire, it is always answered, every single time.

Three Points to Your Creation

There are three points to this fulfilling legacy that is yours: The first point in creation is the desire, or asking. That happens just by your association with your experience. So, the asking happens.

The second point is the answering to that asking. Universal forces, some call it God Force, we call it Creative Life Force — always gives the answer in the moment of the asking.

The third point: You, who is asking, must then receive. You must be in the place where you allow the thing that you are asking for.

So, if there's something that you have been wanting that is not yet manifesting in your experience, it isn't because of one or two: It isn't because you haven't asked, and it isn't because the Universe has not yielded it. It can only be that you are not in the receiving mode.

The Satellite Dish Receiver

You may have seen the Monster Bus that Jerry and Esther are moving about in. On top of it is a satellite dish. So when they come into a campground, Esther will say to Jerry, "Where is Houston?" She wants to know, because somewhere over Houston is the satellite that is going to beam the television signal to their dish. And Jerry will say, "It's off that way." And Esther will look to see if there is a tree between her dish and what she thinks the satellite position is. And if it looks clear, she gets out a chart that tells her what the elevation should be set at, depending upon where they are on the planet in relationship to this satellite dish, and then she pushes some buttons which set the elevation on the dish. And then the little dish begins to turn around and around on the top of the motor coach, until it locks on to the signal from the satellite.

If they do not have the elevation set properly, that little dish just turns around and around, and around. It would work its heart out. It would spin all night long. (Every now and again it does.) But if it is not in the proper receiving mode, they do not have the satisfying results that they are looking for.

> Three Points of Creation:
>
> 1. Your Desire Asks.
>
> 2. Universe Answers .
>
> 3. Allow Your Desire to Manifest.

Sometimes we see you that way. You are willing to put forth endless effort. You'll work 24 hours a day. There is no end to the work or struggle that you are willing to put forth in order to try to achieve. But if you are not in the proper vibrational mode, no matter how much energy or effort or time, or money you put into your endeavor — you don't lock on.

Am I In The Receiving Mode?

Whether it feels good or bad is the indicator of whether you are in the receiving mode or not. So it is always accurate to say that whatever you are living, abundance or poverty, wellness or sickness, joy or despair — *whatever you are living, in this moment, is a perfect vibrational match to your mode of allowing. Whatever you're getting, that is where you've got your dish focused.*

Pretend that there are 100 satellites in the sky, some of them thrill you when you hook up with them, some of them horrify you when you hook up with them, some of them amuse you when you hook up with them, and some of them depress you when you hook up with them. But the operative words are: *You* hook up with them. It is your vibrational countenance that is making all of the difference.

Do you receive the Well-being that is being offered to you? Or are you holding yourself in some sort of tension without even knowing you're doing it?

Continued on page Cat44

The Light of My Life

All of your tapes continue to become increasingly clear, magnificent and inspiring. You, Abraham, are the light of my life for the past six years. Your teachings have brought extraordinary transformations into all areas of my life — which seems like a fairy tale unfolding and continuing to enchant and delight me. Thanks to your guidelines, my former existence of survival and confusion has developed into a new realm of abundance, creativity and enthusiasm.

Esther and Jerry, I send to you both great love and appreciation for the precious knowledge you are so playfully bringing to this planet. By the way — what about a trip to Paris?

With many affectionate and warm wishes from the heart,

KI - France

A Treasure of Pure Positive Energy

For over seven years I've been listening to Abraham's teachings. It's impossible to encapsulate in a few sentences how much help I've received by putting into practice Abraham's processes and approaches to deliberate creation, and deliberate allowing. My life has changed in wonderful ways — large and small. And, yes, the manifestations are wonderful to enjoy, but the experience of being in the flow of pure positive energy, more and more, is what I treasure! I'm grateful for you both bringing Abraham's teachings to us, and to your staff for the exceptional, loving service they provide.

With a happy, grateful heart,

MJK — England

Appreciates Spiritual Food

Sometimes I wonder if you have any idea how much you have benefited the lives of so many. Thank you for all the spiritual food you have given me the past few years. Thank you for all the long hours of work and travel you do to bring Abraham to us. You are so very appreciated.

Much love,

MB — TX

From Skeptisim to "Magic"

Having just been introduced to your work (or that which you have received/collected from Abraham) I simply wanted to say that my initial skepticism was so quickly dissipated by this one Newsletter/Workshop that I am, frankly, both amazed and delighted. That my confusion has been lifted is unquestionable.. Thus, I conclude, it (that which you have shared) must be so. Your analogies are so clear and easy to relate to (as were the Parables of Jesus), thus the same "magic" occurs... I relate to your message and am uplifted by it.

Thank you,

DB — NY

Love ❤ Appreciation ❤ Love

Wow! I'm In CD Heaven

Thank you for your recent upgrade to CD's. My new truck had no tape player. So I asked! And, then forgot about it. Then, BAM! Right out of the blue. Your announcement, and now: Wow, I am in heaven! Thank you! Thank you!

All of my needs are provided for, and more. Thanks for being my path of least resistance for the pleasures of CD. What a life!

Love you folks. I go into your Happy space often. Thanks for the Energy!

PP — CT

Quarterly Journal Fits Her Bag

Thank you so much for the "Introduction to Abraham" CD! The sound quality is excellent — your products just go from strength to strength.

I have not yet received the latest Quarterly Journal and catalog, and I would be grateful if you would advise me whether they have been sent out yet. Your Website has been updated to include the new issue, and I have really enjoyed reading the articles there, but the journal contains info about new tapes that I enjoy reviewing — and, it is the perfect size to fit into my bag to read at work.

Many thanks for your time,

JC — England

Study Group Video Seminar

Our study group will be holding a full day seminar watching the latest video tape offered by Abraham-Hicks. There will be 8 of us — 4 of whom have not yet been to a live seminar.

We decided we'd keep exactly to the format of a live seminar — complete with "segment refreshment" breaks on schedule.

We are so enjoying our weekly cassette series — and are eagerly looking forward to what is on the video.

Much love to you all,

B&L&J&D&C&J&E — Internet

Loves the CDs

I love the CD's, and I love all of you for all you do to keep us in the know, and on our toes, and up to date with what is going on. I can hardly wait for each new CD arrival... as I said to Jerry, they just seem to get shorter and shorter every week. Have a marvelous holiday season and keep us abreast of everything going on on the road and at home.

Much love,

CH — TX

Lost 170 Pounds

I have lost over 170 pounds since I started listening to your tapes. I have the pictures to prove it. This worked for me and has changed my life in every way.

Thank you for being a wonderful messenger, Esther.

DM — CA

Continued on page <None>

STARTER SET: CASSETTES

YOUR STARTER SETS WILL ARRIVE IN A STURDY ALBUM and the recordings (CD or Cassette) included are:

- **INTRODUCTION TO ABRAHAM**
  — A valuable overall perspective of Abraham's basic teachings — and about Jerry & Esther.
- **LAW OF ATTRACTION**
  — Learn how this most powerful Law in the Universe affects your daily life.
- **LAW OF DELIBERATE CREATION**
  — Use this Process for creating your life deliberately, rather than by default.
- **LAW OF ALLOWING**
  — Your Well-being is natural. Learn how to free yourself as you are freeing others.
- **PROCESS OF SEGMENT INTENDING**
  — You will learn, here, how to use your natural power always to your advantage.

...Esther and I are extremely pleased to be able to offer this Starter Set to those of you who are ready for this delicious experience of upliftment.

CASSETTE STARTER SET — $35.00
(AB-1 thru AB-5)

To order, call (830) 755-2299
or see ordering instructions on page 33.

This is it!

IF YOU WANT TO GET A SOLID FOUNDATION OF UNDERSTANDING before you move forward into the teachings of Abraham — this spectacular series is it!

IF YOU WANT TO GUIDE A FRIEND to the clear basis of the life-enhancing perspectives that Abraham has been teaching us since 1985, then this Abraham-Hicks Starter set is it!

IF YOU WANT A SET OF RECORDINGS THAT YOU CAN RELISTEN TO FOR YEARS — and with each listening hear something "new" and valuable — then this is it!

THIS STARTER SET CONTAINS the remastered and edited versions of the original five powerful and popular recordings that Abraham delivered in the beginning of their interaction with us.

THE ORIGINAL ANALOG TAPES HAVE BEEN LOVINGLY EDITED to the 74 minute format; the sound has been professionally remastered — and they are a joy to experience.

CD-1 Introduction To Abraham
CD-2 Law of Attraction
CD-3 Law of Deliberate Creation
CD-4 Law of Allowing
CD-5 Segment Intending Process

CD STARTER SET — $45.00
(CD-1 thru CD-5)

G-SERIES TAPES — SUMMER, 2001

Lock On To Your Receiving Mode

The more you are deliberately choosing thought, the more aware you will be when you have found the thought that you are reaching for. Oh, it is such fun to be a deliberate creator, to stand in the middle of something, and out of it get a new idea, and then to recognize that you are vibrationally not in harmony with your new idea. And then to realize, "Ah, I have something new to reach for." And then, glory of all glories, you now have a new platform with a whole new set of contrasting experiences that give birth to yet another rocket of desire.

Ah, to be focused in a human body with Source Energy flowing through you, friends, it just does not get any better than that. You said, "I will go forth and I will follow my joy, and my joy will lead me to the connection of my Source, and I will fulfill my reason for being." Not once did you say, "I will go forth, find things that are wrong, worry about them with the others, pinch myself off from God Force, and croak from a place of dissatisfaction." Not once did you ever say that.

"I will go forth, understanding that everyone gets to choose whatever they are choosing. I will look for the thought that aligns me with Source, and I will live happily ever after. And I will leave the rest of them to do the same." That's what you said.

You said, "I will go forth and find contrast that will give birth to desire — so that I can help the expansion of the Universe. And I will find vibrational harmony with thoughts that feel good — so that the Source Energy can flow through me here and now."

San Antonio, TX — 4/21/01

G-3/24/01 — Busy healer has received shocking diagnosis. Teen advocacy, and this body of work. She can't struggle her way to success. He's leaving her, but not for another. She enrolled in "Sex and Love Addicts" group. Here's the way to destroy the love. Are cyclic economic business slumps natural phenomenon?

G-4/7/01-A — Do dollar desires thwart his musical skills? Does appreciation of "temporary" job trap him? Do positive thoughts negatively affect her desires? What's up with his thrilling "goose bumps"? His new project feels like something big. Wealthy, artistic mentor lives with dreaded disease. Is All-That-Is a bearded old man?

G-SERIES TAPES SUMMER, 2001

4/21/01 — Fears and dreads her kind gentle horse. Can disconnected Union cause her job loss? Abraham gives a social activist some compliments. Athletics, and balance of mind and heart? Gene manipulation, consequences and child's chosen fate? When a belief runs counter to his desire? In any moment, you have a choice.

4/30/01-B — Singer fears finding a vocal cord lump. Should she intercede in her sister's homelessness? At her age, should she fear illness? When does surgically cutting it out help? Why doctors deny her vertigo and candida. Why hasn't sculptor manifested "grossly expensive" toys? Why Abraham chose him from the questioners.

5/8/01-A — The ratio between your desires and beliefs? Eternal Beings will never get it done. Future of email, message boards and search engines? Why are banker's finances and health impacted? How are you judging other's financial standards? Discussing some aspects of Alzheimer's disease. How much of Us came with us?

5/8/01-B — His issue (subject): attracting significant relationship. Humorist questions concept of "natural born leaders". She doesn't believe humans have personal choices. Still killing and molesting whales and kids? To make upcoming interfaith marriage feel good? Cocreating the essence of newly wed's merged desires? "Senior" wants more lifetime with newest lover.

5/19/01 — Consciously locking on to your receiving mode. Addicted to the struggle for trivial wants. Feeling guilty about unbalanced addiction to work. Drug addicted daughter has gone her separate way. No healing ever takes place in condemnation. "Tough" doesn't belong in the same sentence with "love". She teaches vacillating alternative high school children.

6/2/01— Does the Spiritual vie with physical manifestation? Did financial imbalance influence mother-daughter hospitalization? Can't get over death of her dog. Bankrupted, but really wants to reimburse benefactors. Not an "alcoholic", but the craving continues. "I'm not getting any younger", gets what? You are a manifestation long dreamed of.

6/9/01 — When emotions agree with your own desire. Is a disease hiding in her spine? Have you ever grieved an animal's death? Wondering about transitioned friends as guardian angels. To unhook from her past value systems? But what about having compassion or empathy? Daughter's a star in a square hole.

6/23/01 — Good feels good, and bad feels bad. Substitute teacher is coping with rotten kids. Will humans finally eliminate all other species? Was childhood contrast a platform for teaching? The expanding business of modifying "rebellious" ones. Abraham's positive definition of the term, "blending". British "Vagina Monologues" lifted her chronic fatigue.

When you expose yourself to contrast, you expose your Inner Being and All-That-Is to the same contrast. As you conclude a new desire, you summon Life Force forward into this leading edge experience, and whether you are allowing it to flow through you or not, All-That-Is benefits from that.

Boulder, CO — 6/2/01

We're not here to save the Universe. The Universe doesn't need saving. We're not here to help the Universe expand; the Universe can't help but expand. We're here to assist you in getting into a receiving mode so that you can be the receiver of the benefit that you are providing for the Universe at large.

Tarrytown, NY — 4/7/01A

It's not necessary for you to exacerbate your contrast with struggle in order to get it into a higher place. It is not necessary to suffer in order to give birth to desire. But when you have suffered and you have given birth to desire, so what? You've got a desire. Turn your attention to the desire. Think about where you're going and never mind where you've been. Don't spend any more time justifying any of that stuff.

San Antonio, TX — 4/21/01

The Universe can please all of you at the same time. "Well, how can that be? If I want to live in the mountains and she wants to live at the ocean, how could the Universe possibly please us both?" And we say, as each of you gets to the *essence* of why you want what you want, and are not pointing at the other and saying, "No, no, not that, please not that," the Universe can fulfill both.

Be playful. Know that it's going to be alright no matter what. Have as much fun as you can. Be as easy as you can. Don't take anything very seriously, because everything blows over, good and bad. You can't stand still. So nothing lasts very long. The best of experiences you must move beyond — and the worst of experiences you must move beyond. Don't make where you are too big of a deal. Let it be what it is: It's a moment in time where you have the choice to feel good or feel bad. That's all that it ever is.

Portland, OR — 5/8/01B

If you get a diagnosis that is not what you want to hear, the tendency is to say, "Oh, my god! how did I get so far away from something I want so much?" And we say, it isn't big like that at all — it's just a series of little things. It is the, "I could choose this thought which feels good, or this thought which doesn't feel so good. But I've developed a pattern for what doesn't feel good. And so, it is the daily dose of not being in the receiving mode that keeps me not in the receiving mode." And that's all that it is!

San Rafael, CA — 3/24/01

As you don't allow the Well-being in, it shows up in shadows in your life that are illnesses in your body, and deprivation of things that you want. Then you assign those things labels, and over time you come to believe that that is a reality that has a source somewhere. And then you develop whole bodies of information to protect yourself from the "evil source" that never existed to begin with.

Tarrytown, NY — 4/7/01A

Quarterly Quotes
from Abraham-Hicks

Don't let any place that you are standing frighten you. All it is, is a byproduct of some Energy alignment, which only gives you stronger clarity about what you want — and, most importantly, greater sensitivity about whether you're in a receiving mode or locked off of it.

San Rafael, CA — 3/24/01

There is no condition that you cannot modify into something more, any more than there is any painting that you can paint and not like and just paint over it again. There are many limiting thoughts in the human environment that make it feel like it is not so, as you have these incurable illnesses, or these unchangeable conditions. But we say, they are only "unchangeable" because you believe that they are.

San Antonio, TX — 4/21/01

You might say, "How do I know if I'm in a receiving mode or not?" And we say, you always feel good when you're in a receiving mode. When someone offers you a compliment, do you receive it, or do you sort of just shrug it off? There's something about believing that you must justify your existence through your effort or through your perseverance, through your struggle. And many of you just have not practiced the receiving mode.

Spokane, WA — 5/19/01

If we were standing in your physical shoes, that would be our dominant quest: Entertaining Yourself, pleasing Yourself, connecting with Yourself, being Yourself, enjoying Yourself, loving Yourself. Some say, "Well, Abraham you teach selfishness. And we say, yes we do, yes we do, yes we do, because unless you are selfish enough to reach for that connection, you don't have anything to give anyone, anyway. And when you are selfish enough to make that connection — you have an enormous gift that you give everywhere you are.

San Antonio, TX — 4/21/01

You are always better to stay on subjects that feel good in your own mind. In conversations with a friend, you are always better to talk about what feels good — because when you're talking about what feels good, you're in the receiving mode.

Sacramento, CA — 4/30/01B

What you want and why you want it, is usually the purest form of your vibration. The easiest way to let it in, is by talking about what you want and why you want it.

Portland, OR — 5/8/01A

You just have to be who you are. The best you can do is be certain that you are connected to your Source Energy, and let everybody else figure it out for themselves. Some of them will adore you, some of them will hate you — and none of it has anything to do with you.

Choose what feels good to you and leave everybody else to choose what they want. Don't spend any time saying, "They should choose differently and they'd feel better." Instead say, "They're choosing whatever they're choosing; I'm choosing what I'm choosing, and I'm feeling good while I'm choosing it." And let that be the end of it.

Portland, OR — 5/8/01B

QUESTIONS AND ANSWERS

Still Killing and Molesting Whales and Kids?

Guest: People are still killing whales and killing each other, and molesting kids. And in that balance of not putting my attention to it, then I think that, somehow, I'm saying that that's okay. I'm very idealistic, and there's this discord, and I don't really know how to manage it.

Abraham: As you see things not wanted, and you feel that uncomfortable feeling as you see it, and within that, you feel a rocket of desire within you that things be differently — now your work is to find harmony with your own desire. Every time you turn back and look at things that are not as you want them to be, you are in discord with your own rocket.

There are those that would say to you, "Well, we need you to keep looking at the problem, because we've discovered that we can motivate you to the action that serves us more by keeping you looking at the problem, by keeping you aggravated about all of this."

What you're wanting to say is, "I felt the aggravation; I felt the rocket of desire; I asked the Universe, on your behalf, for a resolution. I know that when anyone asks, the Universe always answers. So help's on the way. And I'm going to do my best about helping us all to *receive* the help that is on the way, by holding myself in vibrational harmony with the desire that I have identified."

There are so many well meaning people who see the contrast, give birth to the rocket of desire, feel it powerfully, shout it to the Universe — and the Universe is answering. And then, they're campaigning against what's wrong and holding themselves apart from the solution. *Even though solutions are happening all over the world, they never have access to them, because they are vibrationally so different from the solutions, that even though solutions are happening, they never get to see a glimpse of them.*

We wouldn't attempt in any way to try to convince you that there are not things that are happening in your world that you don't want to happen. But, looking at the things that you don't want, will never make your world more as you want it to be. It will only drag you down into the discord of that.

As a creator, you are better off with those things you don't want in your world, than if your world was, by your standards, perfect in every way, because those things cause you to reach beyond what-is. And if you do not find reason to reach beyond what-is, then you stand still, and none of us can do that. There is only motion forward. Contrast assures that.

We are *all* free, or *none* of us are free. And so, if you like being able to choose the things that you like to choose — then it must be all right with you that others choose the things that they want to choose.

"Oh, that's so hard! It's so hard. I want them to choose, within reason, only things that I would choose." And we say, then somebody gets to choose what you would choose. And you say, "Well, can't we just all agree on what's alright for us to choose?" And we say, how's that working out for you, now?

Today there are bombs being dropped on nations that choose other than you would have them choose — for no reason other than that they are choosing other than you would have them choose.

You say, "Our way of government is the only way that is acceptable. And we will snuff out all others who are choosing otherwise." And we say, well, where does that one end?

It turns out that it is all being orchestrated from that Broader Perspective. Let's say that some of you get very influential. And you manage to offer your brand of beliefs in such a way that everybody on the planet today, just for a moment, at about

4:30 this afternoon, believes as you believe. Just for that moment, you finally got it done — but, then, tomorrow a whole avalanche of new spirits, renegade spirits, come forth into new bodies with whole different sets of ideas and intentions of everything that you have orchestrated.

The balance of intent is coming forth from that broader Non-Physical Perspective, and the variety is supreme, because out of that variety, each genius consciousness gets to choose something more.

The discord and the squalor and suffering and the poverty and the negative emotion, and the illness, all the bad stuff that you see or hear about in your physical environment — is not because blessed spirits are coming forth and choosing bad things. In every single case, every bit of that suffering or sickness, or sadness, is because somebody's locked off their signal momentarily.

You don't need to worry about the choices. It's not because the choices are there, that people are making horrible choices. In fact, the

> We are *all* free, or *none* of us are free. And so, if you like being able to choose the things that you like to choose — then it must be alright with you that others choose the things that they want to choose.

Continued on page Cat40

A Twelve Point Synopsis
of Abraham-Hicks' Teachings

1 *You Are a Physical Extension of That Which is Non-Physical.*
All-That-Is, or that which you call God, is not finished and waiting for you
to catch up. You are the leading edge of thought, here seeking more: more of
all that feels good to you, more of that which is fresh and gloriously uplifting.
(You are, in essence, bringing heaven to earth.)

2 *You Are Here in This Body Because You Chose to Be Here.*
You chose the opportunity to experience this delicious contrast in time and
space, and with great anticipation you came to co-create with other joy-seek-
ing beings, to fine-tune the process of deliberate thought. (What, where,
when and with whom you create are your choices, too.)

3 *The Basis of Your Life is Freedom; the Purpose of Your Life is Joy.*
You are free to choose to discover new avenues for your joy. In your joy
you will grow, and in your joyous growth you will add to the growth experience of All-That-Is. (However, you are also free to choose bondage or pain.)

4 *You Are a Creator; You Create With Your Every Thought.*
By the Universal Law of Attraction, you are attracting the essence of whatever you are choosing to give your attention to — whether wanted or unwanted. And so, you often create by default. But you can know by how your emotion feels if what you are attracting (creating) is what you are wanting or if it
is not what you are wanting. (Where is your attention focused?)

5 *Anything That You Can Imagine is Yours to Be or Do or Have.*
As you ask yourself why you want it, the essence of your desire is activated,
and the Universe begins to bring it to you. The more intense your positive
feelings, the faster it is coming to you. (It is as easy to create a castle as a but-
ton.)

6 *As You Are Choosing Your Thoughts, Your Emotions Are Guiding You.*
Your loving Inner Being offers guidance in the form of emotion. Entertain
a wanted or unwanted thought, and you feel a wanted or unwanted emotion.
Choose to change the thought and you have changed the emotion — and you
have changed the creation. (Make more choices in every day.)

7 *The Universe Adores You for it Knows Your Broadest Intentions.*
You have chosen to come to earth with great intentions, and the Universe constantly guides you on your chosen path. When you are feeling good, you are, in that moment, allowing more of that which you have intended from your broader perspective. (You are Spirit Incarnate.)

8 *Relax into Your Natural Well-being. All is Well. (Really It Is!)*
The essence of all that you appreciate is constantly flowing into, and creating, your reality. As you find more things to appreciate, your state of appreciation opens more channels that allow more for which to feel appreciation. (As you think, you vibrate. As you vibrate, you attract.)

9 *You Are a Creator of Thoughtways on Your Unique Path of Joy.*
No one can create in your experience, for no one can direct or limit where you can direct your thought. There are no limits to your joyous journeys to experience. On the path to your happiness you will discover all that you want to be or do or have. (Allowing others their experiences allows you yours.)

10 *Actions to Be Taken and Possessions to Be Exchanged Are By-products of Your Focus on Joy.*
On your deliberately joyous journey your actions will be inspired, your resources will be abundant, and you will know by the way you feel that you are fulfilling your reason for life. (Most have this one backwards, therefore most feel little joy in their actions or their possessions.)

11 *You May Appropriately Depart Your Body Without Illness or Pain.*
You need not attract illness or pain as an excuse to leave your body. Your natural state — coming, remaining or leaving — is that of health and Well-being. (You are free to choose otherwise.)

12 *You Can Not Die; You Are Everlasting Life.*
In grace, you may choose to relax and allow your gentle transition back into your Non-Physical state of pure, positive Energy. Your natural state is that of Foreverness. (Have fun with all of this! You can't get it wrong, and you'll never get it done.)

PS It is not necessary for even one other person to understand the Laws of the Universe or the processes that we are offering here in order for you to have a wonderful, happy, productive Life Experience — for you are the attractor of your experience. Just you!

Jerry & Esther Hicks — 11/95 (www.abraham-hicks.com)

FOCUSED IN OUR NOW, the only point in which we have the power to create — neither speculating into the future nor reminiscing into the historical past — ABRAHAM speaks, primarily, toward that practical information which we can personally learn to deliberately apply to our current experience and thereby gain beneficial results....From their broader perspective, unencumbered by your cultural beliefs, ABRAHAM reaches into a place, within you, of clear, primal acknowledgement, from which you will repeatedly hear that enthused inner "voice" reminding you, "I knew that!"

As you experience these Special Subject tapes, expect a fresh state of joyous becoming, for ABRAHAM'S words will stimulate you to a new beginning. Retain the beliefs that are of value to you, and learn to become unaffected by any acquired beliefs or influences that have been a hindrance. ABRAHAM guides us, first, to harmony with our Inner Being, and then all else falls into perfect alignment.

In order to build a foundation of an understanding of Abraham's teachings, begin with the tapes AB-1, *Free Introduction To Abraham,* through AB-6, Great Awakening and Blending, and then progress through the *Special Subject Tapes Series*—as per the order of your interest. Each tape addresses different levels of awareness, and as you repeatedly listen to them, as you are moving forward, you will continually be achieving new insights and experiences.

Order a single at $9.95, 3 or more at $7.75, or order 5 or more, and receive a complimentary (while available) 12 space cassette album.
ORDER ANY COMPLETE SET OF 10 TAPES FOR ONLY $77.50 (PLUS S/H)
See page 33 for ordering information, or call (830) 755-2299.

AB-2 *LAW OF ATTRACTION* * — The most powerful Law in the universe. It affects every aspect of your daily life. A Law which is, whether you understand that it is or not. Specific processes are offered here to help you learn how to harness this Law — to get what you want.

AB-3 *LAW OF DELIBERATE CREATION* * — Discover the ecstasy of understanding universal Laws which are absolute — no matter what the circumstances. Without an understanding of this universal Law, it is as if you are playing in a game where the rules are not understood, so it is not only impossible to know if what you are doing is appropriate, but you do not know how to win the game. The rules of the game of life are clearly offered here.

AB-4 LAW OF ALLOWING * — Of all things that you will come to understand through this physical life experience, nothing is more important than to
become an allower. In becoming an allower, you are free of the negativity that
binds you. Learn the joyful difference between tolerating and allowing — and
experience the blissful difference in every relationship you have.

AB-5 SEGMENT INTENDING — Our futures are individually paved by
the steady stream of thoughts we set forth. We are literally creating our future
life as we direct our thoughts of this moment into the future. Discover the
magnificent power you hold in this moment — and learn how to use that power
always to your advantage.

AB-6 GREAT AWAKENING, BLENDING — You have deliberately and
excitedly chosen this time to be physical beings upon this planet, because you
knew in advance that this would be the time when many — not all — physical beings would recognize the broadness and great value of their being. Follow this step-by-step process for awakening.

AB-7 RELATIONSHIPS, AGREEMENTS — We are all creators as we individually think and plan, but we are also often co-creators as we interact with
others. Most relationships with others are far less than we want them to be.
Find out why. Discover how to rejuvenate unhealthy relationships and attract
new harmonious ones.

AB-8 BODILY CONDITIONS — Nothing is more important to us than the
way we feel and look, and yet so many do not look or feel as they would like to.
There is not a physical apparatus, no matter what the state of disrepair, that cannot have perfect health. Discover the powerful processes to bring your body to
the state of being that pleases you.

AB-9 CHRIST & RELIGIOUS BIBLES — While it can be satisfying to read
and remember the teachings of the great ones who have gone before us, it is ever
more joyous to discover the power of that knowledge within our own being.
Learn the process to go within — as Christ encouraged — to experience the
blissful oneness with Christ.

AB-10 ADDICTIONS — Habits, or compulsions, or addictions can range
from annoying to destroying. Often, long after they are no longer wanted, they
can bind and control your life. As you listen to this recording — you will for
the first time understand exactly what the addiction is, and the simple process
offered here will free you from it.

AB-11 JOYOUS SURVIVAL — While there are seemingly earth shattering
events occurring in greater frequency upon your planet, you need not be affected by them. Discover how to create and control your experience in this seemingly unstable environment.

...I AM A MEDICAL DOCTOR and have not, before, run across material that has this much potential to create health...Have enjoyed Abraham's books and tapes beyond any expectations I had when my mother originally sent them. I would like to subscribe to your "Weekly Tape Program". Thank You.
CHRISTIANE NORTHRUP, MD.— ME

AB-12 PIVOTING & POSITIVE ASPECTS * — If I am the "Creator of my own experience", why don't I have more of what I want? Fostered by an action oriented world, most of you do not understand your true nature of attraction, thus the confusion in why you are getting what you are getting. These processes of pivoting and the book of positive aspects will assist you in the self-discovery of what is important to you, and will put you in the strong, clear place of Well-being, so that you can allow what you want into your experience.

AB-13 SEXUALITY — Love, sensuality and the perfect sexual experience — pleasure vs. shame. This misunderstood issue lies at the heart of more disruption in the lives of physical beings than any other issue. Discover the true nature of your being, and release yourself from the negative turmoil that surrounds the subject of sexuality.

AB-14 DEATH — Aging, deterioration and the perfect death experience — choices vs. chances. The gathering of years is a natural experience. However, deterioration of your physical body is neither natural nor necessary. Be healthy and productive and active and happy until the very day of your chosen re-emergence into the Non-Physical.

AB-15 DOLLARS — Abundance, in perfect flow — gaining the freedom that dollars can bring vs. losing your freedom while gaining your dollars. As there is an abundance of the air you breathe, so there is an abundance of the dollars you seek. Listen and learn how to relax and breathe in the fresh air of freedom offered to you through the abundant flow of dollars.

AB-16 HEALTH, WEIGHT & MIND — The perfect states of weight, health and mind — how can I get there and stay there? Diet plans abound and research continues and yet the number of those unsuccessful at maintenance of satisfactory bodily and mental conditions increases. Understand how your body functions and why you are as you are — and then begin your swift and steady progress toward that which you desire.

AB-17 MATING — The perfect mate: getting, being, evoking one — Attracting vs. attacking. While it is your natural endeavor to co-create with others, there are few who have discovered the bliss of magnificent relationships. Find out how you can experience the joy of a perfect union.

SPECIAL SUBJECT TAPES — VOL II

AB-18 PARENTING — Perfect harmony between my children and me — and me and my parents. Harmonizing vs. traumatizing. While often disconnected from parents, either by death or by distance, your parent/child relationships often have great influence in your experience with your children or with your current life experience. Learn how to perceive what has been in a way that is beneficial to your now rather than destructive. Let that which you have lived be of value.

AB-19 CAREER — The perfect career. What, where and when is it — and what can I do about it now? With so many exterior standards or rules regarding the appropriateness of your behavior or choices — in most cases more confusion than clarity abounds. Use this process to discover and attract that which is perfect for you. Stop the futile backwards approach — and begin creating from the inside out.

AB-20 SELF APPRECIATION — If I am so "Perfect as I am" — then why don't I feel better about me than I do? Selfishness vs. selflessness. Your awareness of your perfection was intact as you emerged into this physical body, but it was soon sabotaged by the critical, comparing, judgmental world that surrounded you. Rediscover your true sense of value and Well-being and perfection.

AB-21 INNER GUIDANCE — Tell me more about my Inner Voice? Because you have thought in terms of being dead or alive, you forget that you are, simultaneously, physically focused while another part of you remains focused from Non-Physical perspective. Once remembering that the inner you exists, you may begin to listen to what your Inner Voice is offering. Here is the process for re-establishing that important conscious connection.

FREE 74 MINUTE INTRODUCTION TO ABRAHAM
Available in Cassette or CD format

A stimulating overview of Abraham's basic message: How to consciously harmonize and interact with your pure, positive Inner Being...How to realize who you are and why you have chosen to be physical in this time...How to joyously and deliberately utilize the Laws of the Universe to Attract all that you are wanting to be or have or do....Also, Jerry & Esther summarize the process of their introduction to Abraham. This recording is a comfortable means to share Abraham with those who seek a new way of realizing a successful life experience. (Order AB-1 or CD-1 Include $5.00 Minimum S/H)

...Since receiving ABRAHAM'S *Free Introductory Tape,* I've listened to it 3 or 4 times. It is concise and very recreatable both in my life and in my work as a consultant...*I wanted to thank you for so much value in this one small tape. I am impressed and moved...Enclosed is my first "real" order.—Texas*

Are Economic Business Slumps Natural Phenomena?

Guest: Is there such a thing as an economic cycle? Is there a natural law to economics, like summer is summer, and fall is fall?

Abraham: Your economics are, in terms of your individual success, your exposure to contrast which gives you your idea of desire, and then your success has to do with your alignment. So, the alignment of your own Energy is the only thing that causes anything to affect you. Of course, your Energy is affected by what you think about other things. And so, your economy is the consensus of the mass consciousness thought, because, as you have become a global world, and as you are all tied into the same media information, you can simultaneously be affected — and therefore mass consciousness is affected — therefore your economic conditions are more worldwide experiences.

These are rip roaring times. This is the leading edge of thought. There is not a reason for there ever to be a decline. And the declines are always false. Always man-made. Never necessary. And they always serve some extremely well.

As we watch your television and we see, through Esther's eyes, the newscasts, we notice that although the good news of your planet is huge in proportion to the bad news — the bad news is what is amplified and given to you.

What the media is showing you, is the bleakest picture, in order to get your attention, because that sells newspapers or television programs, or whatever. And even if they are all doing it, it does not need to affect you. But, it usually does affect you. And as it affects you, then there is a greater ripple effect.

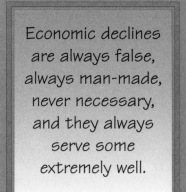

Economic declines are always false, always man-made, never necessary, and they always serve some extremely well.

How could you go through eight years of one presidential administration, having economic booming times, and then days into a new administration, have economic disaster? It is because a handful of people began saying a handful of things that a few billion listened to. And so, it affected a few billion vibrations, and now you're having the ripple effect of all of that. It is a powerful example of the power of mind.

> You are having glorious economic times, and there is not a reason for it to be otherwise for you individually.

There are popular trends and there are unpopular trends. And positive attitude has, as long as you've been in your physical body, not been a very popular trend. It doesn't sell newspapers. It doesn't sell television programs. (It doesn't sell "protection".) If you are in a position that you are wanting to soothe people's troubles, then isn't an aggravation of their troubles beneficial to you? That's sort of what is at the heart of all of that.

You are having glorious economic times. And there is not a reason for it to be otherwise for you as individuals, or you collectively. But don't let what they are doing, collectively, affect you individually. It need not. Begin making statements that always keep you in the receiving mode: "I'm not affected by what's happening outside of me. I'm only affected by the alignment of Energy between my desires. I'm actually benefiting by what's taking place here, because I'm giving more thought to what I am really wanting. I am fine tuning my desires in a more powerful way. I'm pulling more Energy through me than I ever have before. And I'm more deliberately paying attention to when I'm in the receiving mode than when I am not.

"I anticipate that I will thrive even more during these economic times. These are boom times for me. I'm clearer about what I am knowing. I'm in a much better place this time than at any other time. All is really well here, and the Law of Attraction will sort everything out, and we are all doing extremely well."

Continued on page Cat42

NEW VIDEOS NOW AVAILABLE!

These videos were recorded in San Francisco, California, on Saturday, the 26th day of August, of the year 2000.

The Science of Deliberate Creation
The Art of Allowing

This powerful workshop series demonstrates the simple proven techniques that will allow you to easily create anything you desire!

Five, one-hour video cassettes.

Ask for 5V-8/26/00 — $100.00 plus S/H

Included in Part 1:

Abraham tells all that they know; The Law of Attraction; There is no such thing as exclusion; What you are getting is always a vibrational match; Your emotions are your guidance system; Contrast gives birth to rockets of desire; Know that all is well; Ask and it is given; Be more like your cat; Putting death in the proper perspective.

Cat27

VARIOUS SERVICES AND PRODUCTS

MONTHLY SUBSCRIPTION CASSETTE OR CD PROGRAM

We select and edit from as many as 30 new Group Session Tapes that ABRAHAM produces in a month, a 74 minute recording of what we feel contains the most new, inspiring and thought provoking material. And we ship that 74 minute composite recording to the subscribers of the Monthly Subscription Program. *A gift that keeps on giving. Subscription fee: $12.00 per month for cassette and $15.00 per month for CD.*

•   ...Enclosed, please find a check for another one-year subscription to the Monthly Tape Program. *...Every time I replay any one of those tapes, I realize that it has a whole new meaning for me... What a great way to start the day! My profound gratitude to you for sharing this wonderful way of life. — New Jersey*

•   ...You do a wonderful job of editing the Monthly Tapes, because each tape seems to give the answer I need at the time. *Each month gets a little deeper and broader. It is so wonderful to have such guidance. You are what is needed on our planet now. Fondly — Iowa*

WEEKLY SUBSCRIPTION CASSETTE OR CD PROGRAM

For those who want to learn as much as they can "to be and have and do" as fast as they can and are not in the position to personally attend ABRAHAM'S ever evolving workshops, we offer this Weekly Subscription Program: We choose, each week, what we consider to be the workshop with the most stimulating, practical, new ideas — or significant ideas presented from a new perspective — and we form a 74 minute composite recording and ship it to our subscribers. Four cassettes equal one month's billing. *Fill your spare moments with upliftment, flow and forward motion. Subscription fee: $10.25 per week for cassette and $12.50 per week for CD.*

•   ...I'm so enjoying the Weekly Tape Program! How is it that each new tape seems to get better and better? Of course...the power of the Law of Attraction! My life has been transformed in the three years that I have been listening to your tapes. *Every aspect of my life, every relationship I have, has been enriched and enhanced with the knowing of Abraham. I am eternally grateful for this information! With a full and joyful heart. Your friend — Pennsylvania*

WORKSHOPS & WEEKENDS

What do you want to more clearly understand?: Your state of becoming? Finances? Bodily conditions? Relationships? Business/Career? Metaphysicality? Your state of being/having/doing...? To participate in an open group "Questions and Answers" workshop with ABRAHAM, contact Abraham-Hicks Publications at (830) 755-2299 for dates, locations and to make your reservation.

•   ...I was at your workshop in Chicago a few days ago, and I am still floating several feet above the earth. Prior to the workshop I had listened to the tapes and read some of the books and had found this very helpful to me. *Being in the presence of Abraham and watching Esther's physical expression of this profound energy and passion has truly taken me to another level of being able to integrate this information more deeply and easily. Much love. — Illinois*

TO RESERVE OR SUBSCRIBE, CALL OUR OFFICE AT 830 755-2299

PRICE LIST

WORKSHOPS, WEEKENDS, SEMINARS — Details are posted in our Quarterly Journal on page 4. Call (830) 755-2299 for details of activities in your area.

STARTER SET — Cassettes: $35. CD's: $45.00. (See page 10) Album of five of Abraham's most powerful and popular recordings. (See ordering information on page 33.)

WEEKLY SUBSCRIPTION PROGRAM — Cassettes: $10.25 per week. CD's: $12.50 per week. One 74 minute composite of group sessions. Call or write to begin your Weekly Tape or CD Program. (See page 30)

MONTHLY SUBSCRIPTION PROGRAM — Cassettes: $12 per month. CD's: $15.00 per month. One 74 minute composite, each month, that presents the most new practical and inspirational material from Abraham, is selected and mailed to a group of subscribers. Call or write to begin your Monthly Tape or CD Program.

CASSETTE TAPES — $9.95 each. Order 3 or more at $7.75 each — or order 5 or more (in same "Set", "Volume" or "Season") and they will be shipped to you in a complimentary, (a limited offer) convenient 12 space cassette album. Abraham's "AB Series" – Special Subjects 90 minutes, and their "G-Series" 90 minute group session composites are all priced the same: $77.50 for the album sets of 10, $9.95 for singles or $7.75 each when ordering 3 or more. (Plus shipping and handling.)

BOOKS — $15 each. Pay $11.25 when ordering 3 or more. (Plus shipping and handling) Study groups, teachers or dealers, call for volume discount when ordering 9 or more books. (See page 38)

3 TAPE ALBUMS — $30 each (plus S/H). Currently these include our two Sara Books on tape and Abraham's Greatest Hits albums. (See page 49)

NEW! 4 TAPE WORKSHOP ALBUMS (GLUTTON PROGRAM) — $50.00 each (plus S/H) You may now order 4, 74 minute recordings (with flaws and flows) of complete workshops. (CD's, by special order only.)

DAILY PLANNING CALENDAR/STUDY GROUP WORKBOOK — A 768 page planning, envisioning, implementing and manifesting calendar to utilize for your personal creation, or use it as a Course Workbook for a 12 month Group Study. $25.00 (plus S/H). *Check it out; satisfaction guaranteed.* (See page 36)

VIDEO CASSETTES — For prices and details of offerings see page 36 & 37 of our complimentary Catalog (Quarterly Journal, Volume 11) which includes all materials created from 1988 to 2000. (New Videos are now available — See pages 26 & 43)

TRANSCRIPTIONS — Many 90 minute Abraham recordings have been transcribed and are now available for $10 each (plus S/H).

QUARTERLY JOURNAL — "The Quarterly Journal of *The Science of Deliberate Creation*" — Published 4 times a year by Jerry and Esther Hicks. (Current issues are complimentary while in stock. Back issues can be ordered for the minimum packaging and delivery fee of $5 each while supplies last.)

CATALOG — Our complimentary full color 84 page compendium of the first decade of Abraham-Hicks published teachings from 1988 to 2000. Over 500 cassettes, books and videos.

FREE INTRODUCTION TO ABRAHAM-HICKS — This 74 minute recording is an ideal way to introduce the concepts to someone you love. The basics are all here! Specify tape or CD format and include $5 for minimum shipping and handling. (See page 35)

WEB SITE — Visit our new, up-dated Web Site: www.abraham-hicks.com

HOW TO ORDER

ORDER BY MAIL, PHONE, FAX OR INTERNET

BY TELEPHONE — (830) 755-2299

BY FAX — (830) 755-4179

BY INTERNET — www.abraham-hicks.com. (Secured transaction.)

ORDERING

Our order forms are for your convenience, and we will send a replacement order form back to you with each shipment. In order to assist in our efficient processing of your order, please:
- Print all information clearly, or type.
- List each item, its stock number (i.e. AB-1) and its price.
- Pay with your personal check, money order, or use your Master-Card, Visa, American Express or Discover credit card.

WE SHIP UPS, FEDEX OR US POSTAL SERVICE

On larger orders of multiple tapes or books, UPS is usually the fastest, safest, most economical way, but we ship most smaller orders by U.S. Postal. Your order is normally packaged and shipped within 2 working days after we receive it.

INTERNATIONAL ORDERS

Orders outside of the continental U.S. will be shipped US Postal Service (unless UPS is specified) and the additional shipping cost will be charged. Call for current rates. Send U.S. funds only.

PRICE CHANGES

Our posted prices may vary without notice as those who supply us with services or materials may change their prices to us without notice.

DEFECTIVE OR DAMAGED TAPES OR BOOKS

Should you ever receive from us a book that is damaged or a tape that is garbled, blank, bound or broken, please call or write and tell us the title or the series date, and we will replace the item or refund your cost. Due to the spontaneous group interaction with Abraham, the G-Series, or W.T.P. or M.T.P. tapes can sometimes be varied in volume, so we just take the best and ignore the rest. (We are experiencing continual tape quality improvement as we move forward.)

ADD THESE SHIPPING COSTS		
U.S.A.	**CANADA**	**ALL OTHER**
Up to $29.99 ....$5.00.......................................$6.00.................................CALL
$30 to $49.99 ....$7.00......................................$10.00................................CALL
$50 to $99.99 ....$9.00......................................$12.00................................CALL
Over $100 ....$11.00.....................................$13.00................................CALL

We are most appreciative of the many suppliers of services and materials who make it possible for Abraham's words to reach you so efficiently. As costs of doing business are increased, or decreased (taxes, inflation, etc.) to any of our suppliers and passed on to us, we, in turn, through our varied business transactions, reflect those changes back into the international economy.

ORDER FORM

ORDER BY TELEPHONE: (830)755-2299 or FAX (830)755-4179

Order on-line at www.abraham-hicks.com — Or Mail To:

Abraham-Hicks Publications — P.O. Box 690070, San Antonio, TX 78269

NAME _____

ADDRESS _____

CITY _____ STATE _____ ZIP _____

TELE: (HOME) _____ (WORK) _____ (FAX)_____

REFERRED BY: _____

(TO SHIP BY UPS, WE NEED YOUR STREET OR RR NUMBER — NOT A P.O. BOX)

QUAN	STOCK#	ITEM DESCRIPTION	PRICE
	AB-1/CD-1	Tape or CD: Free Introduction To Abraham (min. S/H only)	$5.00
	ST-CD	Starter Set: Abraham's Basics in CD Format @ $45.00	
	ST-TP	Starter Set: Abraham's Basics in Cassette Format @ $35.00	
	ABVONE	Album: 10 Special Subjects @ $77.50	
	ABVTWO	Album: 10 Special Subjects @ $77.50	
	G SERIES	Album: 10 Group Series Tapes @ $77.50 (specify which)	
	ANBI	Book: A New Beginning I @ $15.00	
	ANBII	Book: A New Beginning II @ $15.00	
	CALENDR	Daily Planning Calendar/Workbook @ $25.00	
	SARA-I	Book: Sara & the Foreverness of Friends of a Feather @$15.00	
	SARA II	Book: Sara & Seth, Solomon's Fine Featherless Friends @ $15.00	
	S3SARAI	Book on Tape: Sara I in 3-Tape Album @ $30.00	
	S3SARAII	Book on Tape: Sara II in 3-Tape Album @ $30.00	
		Abraham's Greatest Hits in 3 Tape Albums @$30.00 (specify which)	
Write in desired Individual Special Subject tapes: AB- , Group Series G- , Videos: AV- etc.			

Shipping & Handling Continental USA Additional for International Orders Up to $29.99 . . . . .Add $5.00 $30 to $49.99 . . . . .Add $7.00 $50 to $99.99 . . . . .Add $9.00 Over $100 . . . . .Add $11.00	ADD TOTAL OF ITEMS	
	ADD SHIPPING AND HANDLING	
	TEXAS RESIDENTS, ADD 8.25% SALES TAX	
	TOTAL AMOUNT ENCLOSED	

☐ Personal Check: (Make payable to J & E Hicks — US Funds only)
☐ MasterCard ☐ VISA ☐ American Express ☐ Discover

Card # _____ Exp Date _____

Cardholder's Signature _____

(SARA 3)

Print Name_____

THANK YOU!

Our thanks to you for your role in this joyous co-creation. Your thoughts as we interact, your pondering, questioning, recognizing, knowing and wanting... add to our forward motion and to the fulfillment of our purpose.

We intend to allow ABRAHAM'S *words of perspective, positive guidance and stimulation of thought, to go as far and as fast as they are wanted. At the same time, we intend to continue our abundant, positive, mental, material and spiritual experience — and we do appreciate your contribution of "thoughts, words and deeds."*

Do you have a friend who would enjoy our Quarterly Journal?

Name (Please print) _____

Address _____

City/State/Zip _____

Your name _____

---

* EDUCATORS—TEACHERS—STUDENTS *

Are you involved in education and interested in an uplifting perspective? We can mail to you (at no cost) a copy of Daniel Greenberg's *Free At Last*, highlights of the first 20 years of the remarkable Sudbury Valley School experience. We have a few remaining copies (not for sale) just let us know if you would like one and we'll get it off to you as soon as it is practical.

This book will make your heart sing!

(We ship this book only to the one who is requesting it.)

OUR UNCONDITIONAL
GUARANTEE OF SATISFACTION

We are aware that due to technical or personal idiosyncrasies you may receive a damaged or defective or unwanted item from us — but we will replace it or refund your money (whichever you prefer) just as soon as you call or write and give us the details. Unless we request it, please don't bother with shipping the item back to us. Just toss it away, or pass it on. We want you to be completely satisfied with our products and our service.

Jerry & Esther

Packaging & delivery (S/H) costs are no longer refundable.

FREE CD/CASSETTE
"INTRODUCTION TO ABRAHAM"

...*Yesterday I received the Introduction to Abraham CD! Although I have been working with Abraham's ideas for more than a year, am a member of the "CD of the Month" club, and was very happily present at the workshop at the Biltmore Estate in Asheville, I had never heard the introductory tape. Well, the information on that CD helped me bridge a gap in my thinking about the principles of deliberate creation. And the clarity feels wonderful! Many thanks for the CD, and for all the wonderful work you are all doing!*

With boundless appreciation, — LR — NC

...*Thanks for the wonderful new Introduction CD. Wow! I'm so very pleased! My gratitude, for so much Joy and Well-being that I am now experiencing, is immense. I resonated with the comments from the readers and listeners on the inside of the jacket cover of the CD: "I've been a 'searcher', 'seeker', 'sharer' since I was a teen," except in my case it's been since I was about 5. The next line just floored me, "My middle name was purported to be 'Why?'" How true... I was asking as a child. Especially as a child. I never stopped asking. And thank you for clarifying the role that "contrast" plays in our lives. Yes, all the pieces are finally falling into place. And also "Thank you for helping to put the fun back into my life". My entire experience has pivoted, literally.*

Thanks again — *In absolute bliss* — BF — Canada

This 74 minute professional remastered Introduction to Abraham is now available in cassette or CD format. It's a comfortable way to share Abraham with those who seek a new way of realizing a successful life experience.

Order:AB-1 or CD-1 (Include $5.00 Minimum S/H)

WORDS OF WISDOM FROM THE BROADER PERSPECTIVE

YOU ARE LIVING THE MANIFESTATION OF THE PERFECT DREAM THAT YOU LAUNCHED FROM YOUR GOD SOURCE PERSPECTIVE. I's time for you to start feeling appreciation for the clarity and power with which you chose to be here, and to feel, through connecting with your Inner Being, the satisfaction of it now playing out.

You are the manifestation long dreamed of — bringing endless satisfaction to that which is your Source. And now your Source is here, wanting to express to you ways to help you get back into the loop of joy that you began, even before you made the decision to come here.

Reach for thoughts that feel better; pay attention to the way you feel. And as you bless every emotion, whether it feels good or bad, because you know that it is the indicator of your connection to Source Energy, you regain the feeling with which you came forth into this experience to begin with. And as you regain your memory of why you came forth into this physical experience to begin with, you will be inundated with indescribable joy.

Abraham-Hicks — Boulder, CO — 6/2/01

PRESENTING A POWERFUL 365 DAY COURSE IN SPIRITUAL PRACTICALITY

Habits are usually created slowly. And since a major aspect of the value to you of using this material will be the changing — often slowly — from unwanted habits of thought to habits of thought that are more appropriate to your current conscious desires — *the most common use of this calendar will be as a joyous 365 day journey into a new world of leading edge thought and experience.*

Begin experiencing the power of this calendar at any time. You don't have to wait until the first of next year. However, in order to get into time sequence with the calendar — it is best to start at a month's beginning. Let the first day of your first month be day one (page three) of this calendar.

After over 30 years of studying, teaching and enjoying the art of personal fulfillment, I have long understood the power of clarifying and writing out my decisions in appointment books, journals, organizers, etc. But as the years passed, I became aware that at the most joyous and highly productive seg-ments of my life — I simply carried, daily, a fresh, updated sheet of paper in my pocket. This works!

The first sides of the pages are compilations from the best of the Abraham teachings. The second sides of the pages are designed to accommodate your daily list of things to do. *But as the course progresses, you will discover that the pages will be offering processes and techniques to fit the advancing stages of your progression within these materials.*

Your only power to create your life is in this moment, and the Abraham-Hicks Planning Calendar is designed to focus the purest of your intentions to your todays, the time in which you have your creative power.

In our estimation, this Abraham-Hicks Planning Calendar/Workbook is the most effective tool available for the practical application of "The Science of Deliberate Creation." Utilize it to create and to teach others to create, the perfect (by your ever changing standards) adventure in living.

"If you want to change what you are living,
you only have to change the balance of your thought." — *Abraham*

THE SCIENCE OF DELIBERATE CREATION

Abraham-Hicks Daily Planning Calendar and Study Group Workbook

A 365 DAY COURSE IN SPIRITUAL PRACTICALITY

- The material in this calendar/workbook has been specifically intended as an experiential guide to comfortably change your balance of habits of thought to that which will enrich every aspect of your experience.

- Begin in any month. The pages are left to be dated by you.

- This is a study to do, not a study to simply peruse. It is a study to have fun with in every way that you can imagine.

- The pages are the size of two $100 bills, side-by-side. Tear out a page a day. They are portable. Fold them into your wallet or checkbook, or simply carry them in a pocket. On one side you will find life enriching reminders of some things you may have forgotten and on the other side you can write intentions, ideas, names, numbers. Post them on your mirror, refrigerator, the sun visor of your car...

- Carry a seven day segment or a vacation segment with you when you are away from home — and then file them for future reference.

— *Let the Magic Begin* —

SELF HELP FROM YOUR TOTAL SELF

ORDER: PLANNING CALENDAR (768 PAGES) $25 USA

BOOK: A NEW BEGINNING I

THIS EXTRAORDINARY BOOK is powerfully offered by a group of teachers who call themselves Abraham. They express clearly and simply the laws of the universe, explaining in detail how we can deliberately flow with these laws for the joyful creation of whatever we desire. Abraham describes this as the time of awakening, explaining that each of us chose, with very deliberate intent, this specific time of great change to participate in this physical experience. This is an empowering, life-changing book that will assist you in seeing your personal life experience as you have never seen it before.

...The breakthrough book that started a worldwide interest in Abraham. Now in it's eighth printing, *A New Beginning I* explains in simple terms the eye-opening fundamentals of living a life of health, wealth and happiness. — Texas

COMMENTS:

• Thank you for a delightful book—*A NEW BEGINNING I*—a life changing book...a joyous do-it-yourself book...I have always known this was an "inside job", but I've not known, before, how to communicate well with the "inside." — Germany

• We are thrilled with the data. Everyone we have sent the book to thinks it is the best book they have ever read. — California

• The feedback I've gotten on the many *ABRAHAM* books that I have distributed has been phenomenal and it has come from all over the world. — California

• The first edition of *A NEW BEGINNING I* sold out because readers love the practical ideas of Abraham. In the tradition of Jane Roberts, this refreshing new book reveals a unique blend of new-age thought with the Western desire for "more." An inspiring self-help classic that gets results.

Softcover. $15.00. 218 pages. ISBN 0-9621219-3-2.
(To order, see page 33, or call 830 755-2299).

BOOK: A NEW BEGINNING II

THIS IS AN UPLIFTING BOOK that strikes a chord with the very core of your being. Written by Abraham to assist you in understanding the absolute connection between your physical self and your inner self, Abraham puts this physical life experience into perspective as they explain and define who we really are and why we have come forth as physical beings. This book is filled with processes and examples to assist you in making a deliberate conscious connection with

your own Inner Being, that you might find the awesome satisfaction with this physical life experience that can only come once this connection is made.

...Now in it's seventh printing, *A New Beginning II* contains uplifting new material from Abraham including *Law of Attraction, Law of Allowing,* and the effective use of your *Guidance System.* Includes questions and answers from live workshops, affirmations, and powerful processes for increasing your ability to intentionally create WHATEVER you want. Incredible! A must read! — Texas

COMMENTS:

- Your book, *A NEW BEGINNING II,* has been my constant companion, now marked and circled on page after page...So—UP with the "Fairies of the Universe" and beautiful music and laughter! — France

- ..I hugged the book; I couldn't put it down for two days....You should see my metaphysical library—and of every book I have, this is the clearest! — Germany

- Thank you so much for the book—it is the best yet. I like to open it at random and see what the good word is for the day. — California

- Like the book before it, *A NEW BEGINNING II* is clear, practical, inspiring and empowering with more focus on how to realign with your Inner Being. The bottom line for Abraham-Hicks is to choose to feel good in every moment. From that base of joy you will naturally and easily create what you want for yourself and the world.

Softcover. $15.00. 258 pages. ISBN 0-9621219-1-6
(To order, see page 33, or call 830 755-2299)

Sara and the
Foreverness of Friends of a Feather

...My whole family read this book and we haven't been the same since. My husband, perhaps, was the most moved by it. He actually said that it had such a tremendous impact on him that he looks at life with new eyes. It's like being nearsighted your whole life and then finally getting glasses. Everything becomes crystal clear.

I cannot say enough good things about this life-transforming book. If there is only one book you ever buy, make sure it is this one. You won't regret it! (all ages)

— by Denise Tarsitano in the "Rising Star Series.

THE BOOK

Sara and the Foreverness of Friends of a Feather is a novel about a young girl, Sara, who learns about life through a wise owl named Solomon.

As you settle into this book you will begin to experience Sara's life, almost as if it is your own. You'll discover that the questions that Sara's life uncovers will not be so different from the questions of your own life.

Sara has the benefit of a wise and wonderful mentor who not only knows the answers to all questions, but also understands that words don't teach. Solomon wisely helps Sara to find the answers to her very important questions through her own life experience. And as Sara discovers her answers — you will very likely discover some of your own, as well.

This book will awaken within you wisdom you were born with, that you may have forgotten. It will open you to who you really are. (all ages)

BOOK: Ask for SARA-1 — $15.00 (plus S/H) Softcover.— ISBN 0-9621219-4-0

THE TAPES

Sara and the Foreverness of Friends of a Feather is now available as an unabridged book on tape. Containing three audio-cassettes, this album offers over three hours of inspiring, uplifting and entertaining listening.

At the wheel of your vehicle or doing mundane chores or relaxing with closed eyes, you can now comfortably absorb the pleasure of this extraordinary magical relationship between young Sara and her ethereal, old, feathered owl friend, Solomon...

CASSETTES: Ask for S3S1 — $30.00
(830) 755-2299 (Order form page 33)

Sara and Seth,
Solomon's Fine Featherless Friends

...My family had read the first Sara book and were captivated by its wisdom and clarity. I knew we were in for a treat with this new story, "Sara and Seth", but I had no idea just how much of an impact it would have on all of us.

The sheer brilliance of this unassuming little book with its powerful message (of Well-being) will leave you breathless.

(all ages)

— by Denise Tarsitano in the "Rising Star Series."

THE BOOK

When Seth moves into Sara's mountain town, and right into the middle of all of the secrets of Thacker's Trail, Sara doesn't know what to do with him. She is drawn to him in a strange and powerful way, but the idea of letting anyone in on her unbelievable secrets seems impossible. But Sara soon comes to trust Seth, and together they embark on an even more wonderful experience with Solomon.

Seth has been gathering important questions all of his very short life. He can barely believe his good fortune in meeting Solomon, who understands all things.

You'll enjoy seeing Sara's good life getting even better, and Seth's rather awful life becoming wonderful. And like everyone else, you will love Solomon.

BOOK: Ask for SARA-2 — $15.00 (plus S/H) Softcover ISBN# 0-9621219-7-5

THE TAPES

Sara and Seth, Solomon's Fine Featherless Friends is now available as an unabridged book on tape. Containing three audio-cassettes, this album offers over four hours of inspiring, uplifting and adventurous listening.

Relaxing with closed eyes, you can now comfortably absorb the pleasure of this extraordinary magical relationship between Sara and her new friend of a feather, Seth... plus, her ethereal owl friend, Solomon, makes his welcome reappearance, adding his wise perspective to their/our learning experiences.

CASSETTES: Ask for S3S2 — $30.00
(830) 755-2299 (Order form page 33)

QUESTIONS AND ANSWERS

Continued from page Cat17

more that they feel that they don't have choices, the more locked off they are, and the more choices that feel awful they make. *Those that are acting out in violence, aren't acting out from their place of feeling free and secure. They're feeling bound and insecure. They're frightened. They're fighting for their very life, on vibrational levels.*

It doesn't take many like you to lie in your bed, acknowledge some violence that you worry about, and feel the discomfort of it, and then feel the rocket of desire burst forth, that your children, and children like them, have lovely environments to grow up in. *And then, as you reach for thoughts, in the next 30 days, that cause you to lock onto that feeling of Well-being — you would be amazed at the power of influence that the effort of one individual provides.*

You didn't come to this world because it is broken and needs fixing. You came to this world because it is fantastic and you wanted to be here. But then, when you get here, when you start finding fault with parts of it that don't please you, you sort of negate the balance that you knew would be here that you chose, to begin with. That's why we want you to begin relaxing and allowing everything to be okay for a while.

Your work is to joyously choose thoughts, words and actions that feel good while you choose them. And you say, "Well, that doesn't sound like enough justification for this life experience. How will I separate myself from the others? How will I stand out? How will I become the leader of the pack? How will I get the most stars on my chart? How will I excel?"

The other day we asked a group, "Does it bother you that Source Energy adores 100% of your population? How do you feel about that? Source Energy adores, not just tolerates, not just allows, Source Energy adores 100% of the population." Some are irritated at the idea, because they've been working very hard to be virtuous and praiseworthy. And it's irritating that those not working nearly as hard are still adored.

When you reach this place that it is alright with you, that everything is alright, then you have no reason, ever again, to lock off your signal. That doesn't mean you don't have preferences. But when you no longer are condemning, pushing against, negating, or trying to remove something, then you're no longer a vibrational match to any of that, and then, only Well-being can be your experience.

FOLLOW WHAT YOU KNOW TO BE TRUE. IF IT FEELS GOOD, IT'S RIGHT ON. IF IT DOESN'T FEEL GOOD, IT'S NOT. THAT'S IT, THAT'S ALL THERE IS TO THAT.

From Abraham-Hicks Workshop
Portland. OR — 5/8/01B

NEW VIDEO: DEATH & LIFE

Mike and Karen Sherlock, our videographers and long time friends, surprised us with this spectacular special edition of *Abraham, on Death & Life.*

Especially timely is an excerpt from the San Rafael workshop taped in September, 2000. It seems most revealing of the stance of the mass consciousness, in that, one year before the vengeful September 2001 event, that one of the questions asked of Abraham was regarding those who would "give up their lives to blow up buildings."

Esther and I reviewed this video last night, and we were both thrilled by it. (Esther, especially enjoyed it because she had the opportunity to "see and hear" Abraham much like the rest of us do.)

And Abraham's closing segment, "Audio Ecstacy" is as good as it gets!

SUBJECTS INCLUDED:

- **Realize that there is no death.** (12:00)
- **We are all Eternal Beings.** (8:00)
- **What is it Like for Non-Physical?** (16:00)
- **When you understand death, you can begin to live.** (8:00)
- **When Middle East Fanatics give their lives to blow up buildings.** (7:00)
- **There's no resting in heaven.** (1:00)
- **Abraham offers audio ecstacy.** (6:00)

Order: AV-8 Death & Life — $30.00. Running time: 1 hour
(To order, see page 33, or call 830 755-2299).

When you hear others that are expressing otherwise, sometimes it is to your advantage to stop, just for a brief moment, and ask: what is their reason for perpetuating this? In many cases, they haven't thought it through. But, sometimes the answer will be, it is to their economic advantage to do so. And as you begin to acknowledge how many people are using this to their economic advantage — you won't worry about the economy any more.

Economics has always been about supply and demand. So if you are the diamond dealer and people are digging diamonds up in their back yard, you might want to go find something more rare, like a chunk of coal, or something like that.

There is no shortage. We know that there is no shortage, because we know that when you ask, the Universe has the ability to yield. There cannot be a shortage. All there can be is an individual or a whole bunch of individuals cutting themselves off from the supply of Well-being — by finding one thing or another to be upset about.

Remember, there are the three points... You ask, the Universe yields, and you just must be in the receiving mode. It does not matter what games anybody else is playing. You have the ability to stand in a place of prosperity — no matter what. And so, is there ever, really any shortage? There is never ever, ever, ever, ever any shortage! It is all something that is man's making. Sometimes deliberate, sometimes indeliberate. But it is never reality. It is only a perception of reality.

Life is good, let it be. It is our powerful wanting that you let yourself receive half the benefit that we all receive in our interaction through you. It's time for you to begin letting it in.

There is great love here for you.

> It does not matter what games anybody else is playing. You have the ability to stand in a place of prosperity — no matter what.

From Abraham-Hicks Workshop
San Rafael, CA — 3/24/01

NOW AVAILABLE

The *Monthly Subscription Program* and *Weekly Subscription Programs* and the *Free Introduction to Abraham* recordings can NOW be ordered on CD or Cassette.

Weekly Cassette Program ....$10.25 per week
Weekly CD Program.........................$12.50 per week
Monthly Cassette Program ....$12.00 per month
Monthly CD Program ....$15.00 per month
Introduction To Abraham................Free + $5.00 S/H

There is only a source of Well-being. You may be letting in the fullness of that Well-being, or you may be pinching it off a bit — but depending upon how you're doing with that, you are living your life experience.

The way you feel is your indicator of whether you're letting it in. Letting what in? Letting in Well-being. Letting in the clarity that is really you, and letting in the abundance that is natural to you. Letting in your resilience, your physical stamina, and your flexibility. Letting in your ability to intuitively know your path. Letting in your sensitivity to your surroundings, your opportunities to expand, and your joy and appreciation. Letting yourself be who you really are. Letting in whatever you desire.

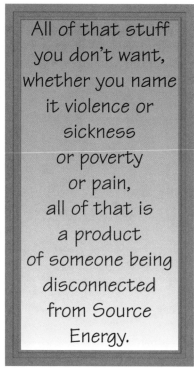

All of that stuff you don't want, whether you name it violence or sickness or poverty or pain, all of that is a product of someone being disconnected from Source Energy.

there is the factor of allowing: how much allowing is going on. When you see someone in poverty, in anger, in violence, in pain, or in sickness, rather than judging the correctness of their desire, which none of us have the ability or the right to do, instead just stop and evaluate (if you are wanting to be of value) whether they are connected fully to the Source of Well-being, or whether they have found some way of pinching themselves off.

We believe that you will never again be in a place of not understanding why you or anyone that you are observing is getting what they're getting. You can tell by the things they say, and by the way they are feeling, whether they are holding themselves in a vibrational match to their own desires or not.

Why You Feel What You Feel

All of that stuff you don't want, whether you name it violence or sickness or poverty, or pain, all of that is a product of someone being disconnected from Source Energy. Disconnected is too strong a word; you can never be disconnected, you just get it pinched off pretty good.

Two factors are involved in what makes people feel the way they are feeling: There is the factor of desire: how much focused desire there is. And then

You Are Here Because It's Fun

We don't need to teach you about what to want. That part comes naturally to you. It's not anybody's business what you want, anyway; you are freedom based Beings who get to choose. We don't need to tell you about who you are from Non-Physical; you innately know who you are: *You are Source Energy expressing in this physical body. You're not here to prove some kind of worthiness. You're not here to fix something that is broken. You are here as expanding Beings to assist with the expansion, not because it needs your assistance, but because it is fun. It is fulfilling.*

In this inevitably expanding Universe, you genius creators said, "I will go forth into this contrasting experience, where all kinds of choices will be laid before me. And out of this buffet of opportunities, I will conclude — sometimes unconsciously, sometimes fully consciously — new desires; in some cases, desires that have never been unto this Universe, or any other, ever before. And when that new rocket of desire is born within me, my work is done, because when that rocket is born, the asking is now in place. And when the asking is in place, the answering is in place. And so, the expansion of the Universe happens joyously, naturally, creatively, and eternally".

We come forth in response to your asking, not because your lives are inadequate, but because it thrills us when you deliberately line up with your own desire. It is not our desire to guide your desire.

When you made the decision to come forth into this physical experience, you knew there would be enormous variety that would help you come to conclusions. And you knew that you were, then, a part — and would, in this body, be a part — of a Universe that is freedom based. Which means, no one seeks to control that which you identify as your desire.

This gathering is not about that. Desire happens. This gathering is about assisting you in achieving vibrational harmony with your own desire, so that you can, right now this red hot minute, express yourself in the fullest sense of the word.

None Need Fear An Aligned One

Now, that's frightening to some. They say, "Abraham, if everyone really felt free to desire anything, wouldn't we need to hide out from a lot of them?" And we say, we don't think so, because everything that everyone wants — no matter what it is — is always because they believe they would feel better in the having of it. And we have noticed that when you align with that which makes you feel better — no one would ever need to fear you.

Align Your Thoughts and Desires

As with all analogies, our satellite dish analogy is not perfect. The biggest difference between it and what's happening with you is that your contrast, which causes you to give birth to your rocket of desire, sends the signal. In other words, it is your desire that is beaming to you. So when we say you're wanting to align the Energy within you, we're talking about aligning the Energy of your now thought — your habit of thought, your belief, your day-to-day vibrational expression — with the vibration of your desire.

So, you launch the rocket that is sending the signal to you, now all you've got to do is line up with the signal that you've sent to you. In other

> It is not
> our desire
> to guide
> your desire.

words, it is the vibrational harmony between the vibrational meter of your desire and the vibrational meter of your now expression, or your belief, that matters. If you've concluded, through your exposure to contrast, that you desire something different in your experience, and that desire is vibrating here: It is this dream, this idea, that when you first thought about it thrilled you, but now you stand here mostly noticing what-is, talking about it softly to your friends, "Wish this were different; wish this were different; wish this were different;" in every moment that you're talking about what-is, instead of where you're going — instead of what you are desiring — you are holding yourself vibrationally apart from the thing you want. You are not locked onto your signal.

Catch Yourself in the Act

It would be helpful if you would begin to catch yourself in the act of being locked off your signal. Because we hear so many of you saying, "What's going on here? I want it. I've been saying I want it. I know I'm using the right words. I know I've got the right expression on my face. Why isn't it happening?" The answer to that is: it is because you keep doing that thing that you do that locks you off the signal.

Some time ago, Esther went out to the chicken coop and found a possum in the nest where the eggs are, with egg all over its face. She loved it. "Egg on

its face! Imagine that!" Esther said, "I've heard that all my life, and this is the first time I've ever caught someone with egg on their face." And if you could have seen this little possum, with the guilty look on his face, he was the epitome of being caught with egg on his face.

Catch yourself in the act of doing that thing that you do when you are not allowing the Pure Positive Energy to flow; when you're not allowing yourself to be a vibrational match to your own desire.

So what happens is, you tend to evaluate the content of your now experience so fully that you find the more familiar vibration of what-is, rather than finding the better feeling vibration of what you desire. And that, right there, is the only thing, the only thing, that ever holds you apart from anything you want.

Catch yourself in the act of doing that thing that you do.

It's Only A Little Bit of Poison

We tease a little bit. It's like being willing to endure just a little bit of poison. It's like, every day, finding a little poison and just tasting it. It's a little bitter at first, just a little bit. Hmm, doesn't kill you right away. Diminishes your experience almost unnoticeably in the beginning. But then you sort of get a taste for it. It's like it becomes a habit. It becomes so familiar that even though it doesn't really feel good while you do it, it doesn't really give you immediate detrimental results. And so you just sort of lap it up a little bit....

Continued on page Cat48

ABRAHAM'S GREATEST HITS

Here are three dynamic hours of uplifting material skimmed from the five hour San Antonio Workshop, April, 2000. These three tapes are a prime example of Abraham's expanding message of consciously regaining our natural Well-being. Abraham's cocreative, fun-filled dance with the questioners and the audience offers new, exciting words to guide us toward creating our everyday joyous journey. This is the perfect album for those who are asking for more.

THE SCIENCE OF DELIBERATE CREATION
ABRAHAM-HICKS PUBLICATIONS

San Antonio, TX — 4/15/00
(3 hours of Classic Abraham)

TAPE ONE

- To monitor your pile of "Vibrational Sticks".
- Reach for the thought that feels best.
- His Ex-wife and Their Kids Stick.
- Were they divorcing from their happiness?
- The Golden rule or the Platinum Law?
- Human's overlaying vibration: the desire for approval.
- Can't communicate with dead father's Energy.

TAPE TWO

- Is daughter more protected attending church school?
- Who should be controlling your child's mind?
- Will religious beliefs affect her death experience?
- Death experience, likened to Lovable Cat's door.
- What is the mission of my life?
- Can one have freedom without expectations?
- What should she invest in singing career?

TAPE THREE

- When one's mate isn't seeking same "Truth"?
- In every relationship, a guide and a follower.
- Getting past his compulsion to eat sugar.
- Addictions, as cell's compensation for dietary imbalances.
- Why does he get small things faster?
- Look great in mirror or on sailboat.
- Your cells respond to your visualized perceptions.

Order S3SA — $30.00 plus S/H

Continued from page Cat46

Sometimes we visit with our physical friends who feel that they are very far apart from something they want. Maybe their body has been labeled something that is frightening them. Or maybe they have some economic disaster, or a personal relationship disaster. And as they come to us, their attitude about self is, "I must have done something really, really wrong. There must be some major thing that I'm doing or have done that is now keeping me from this thing that I want."

It isn't anything big. It's just the steady habit of holding yourself locked off the signal. It's a whole lot of simple little things that usually don't amount to much more than slight aggravation or slight irritation. It's just that edgy feeling of not being in the place of fully receiving.

When the satellite dish is off the signal only a little bit, there is no picture on the TV screen. You can't get a little bit close to it. It's either locked on or it's not. The same thing is happening with you. When you're locked onto your signal of desire, you feel good. You feel this feeling of exhilaration. You know that you are locked on when you are.

Pay Attention to Emotions

Your emotions tell you everything that you need to know about your relationship with your Source Energy. Your emotions

tell you how specifically focused you are, which means how strong your desire is, and how much of the Source Energy you're summoning through your focused desire, right now. And your emotions tell you whether you are, in this moment, a vibrational match to your desire or not — whether you are in the mode of allowing or receiving, or not.

And so, by paying attention to your emotions, or by paying attention to the way you feel, you are getting a very clear indicator of what your vibrational offering is.

We want you to be aware of your vibrational offering while it is in the emotional stage rather than waiting for it to be in the manifested stage, although that works too. You can pay no attention whatsoever to the way you feel, just offer your thoughts, and therefore your feelings or vibration, all over the place, and the Universe will match you with perfect vibrational matches. And as you receive the manifestation, you can say, "I would have rather this truck did not fall on me." And then, it is a little bit more time consuming to bring yourself back to your fully unflattened state. Although it can be done — it is cumbersome.

You are extensions of Source Energy. And the more you are allowing the fullness of your Source Energy to flow through you — the more you thrive. Source Energy is likened to your electricity that flows

> It isn't anything big. It's just the steady habit of holding yourself locked off the signal.

through your walls. And some of you are having rolling blackouts, we notice. Not only in your houses, but in your day-to-day experience, as you find things that you use as your excuse to pinch yourself off from the Source Energy that is You.

It would be like plugging in your appliances and having only half of the electrical current. And your lights are flickering, sometimes they are on, sometimes they aren't, your buzz saw just turns slowly. And you say, "I am wanting to be hooked up to a stronger grid. I am wanting purer electricity to flow through my system."

Am I Letting It In?

Discover how to clean up your vibration so there is not so much resistance within you, so that you can be the fuller receiver of that which you are asking for. It is not a difficult thing to do, once you are understanding the process —it is really about setting yourself into vibrational harmony with that which feels good. We would encourage you to ask yourself on a regular basis, maybe hundreds of times in every day, "Am I letting it in? Am I letting it in?" Letting what in? You could call it Creative Life Force, God force. "Am I holding myself in vibrational harmony with those things

that I have identified that I'm wanting to experience?"

Why Isn't It Coming To Me?

The only reason that something that you want is not coming to you, is that you are holding yourself in vibrational harmony with something other than what you want. And the good news is: every single time you're doing it, every single time, without exception, you are feeling something less than positive emotion when it happens. So if you are asking yourself on a fairly regular basis, maybe two or three hundred, or a thousand, times every day, and if you're catching yourself in the act of doing it now — it won't take 30 days of being aware that you're doing it now to stop doing it now.

Once you realize what the receiving mode feels like, it is such an easy thing to hold yourself in vibrational harmony with the Well-being that is natural to you. And that is what the Science of Deliberate Creation is about.

You Are Vibrational Beings

You are vibrational Beings much more than you are flesh, blood and bone beings. You are more vibrational, you are more electrical, than you are anything else. And the way that you read the vibration of your

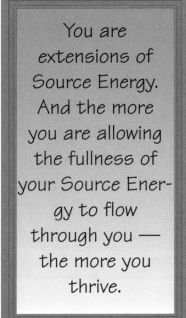

You are extensions of Source Energy. And the more you are allowing the fullness of your Source Energy to flow through you — the more you thrive.

Being is through your emotions. Your emotions tell you everything that you will ever need to know about your relationship with your Source Energy. And we can't think of anything that is more significant for you to be aware of than your relationship with your Source Energy — because the Source Energy is life itself.

When you are fully connected to and fully allowing Source Energy, you are the extension of that. You are that Blended Being. You are allowing the whole of You to flow through and live this physical experience. In that state of being, eagerness would be your most common emotion. You would vacillate between saying things like, "Oh, this is interesting," to "Oh, this is satisfying," to "Oh, don't you love that," to "Oh, I'm really enjoying this," to "Oh, this is interesting…." All of those feelings of life-giving emotion are the natural way that you are, and the way you felt as you came forth into this physical experience, to begin with, — and the way you would always feel once you get the hang of catching yourself in the mode of doing that thing that you do that keeps all of that from happening.

> The only reason that something that you want is not coming to you, is that you are holding yourself in vibrational harmony with something other than what you want.

You Are Eternal Beings

You are eternal Beings, which means you never get it done. How does that feel? You never get it done. If that feels like, "Oh good," then you are hooked up with Source Energy; you are recalling who you are; you are eagerly anticipating the unfolding; you are remembering that the destination has never been what it's about. The destination just gives you something to focus upon so that the Energy flows, so that your journey is exhilarating.

When you realize that you are eternal Beings, that must mean that there's way more before you than there could ever be behind you. In other words, eternity means forever. And so, when you get in sync with eternity, doesn't it make you sort of want to relax and enjoy, and savor?

What's The Big Rush?

What's the big rush? What is the clamoring toward one destination or another? Why not kick back a little bit; take in the perfection of where you stand? Think about where you're going; reach for feelings, past present or future, that feel good — and enjoy who you are in your powerful and pointed now.

Abraham-Hicks Workshops —
Portland, OR — 5/8/01A
San Antonio, TX — 4/21/01
San Rafael, CA — 3/24/01

G-SERIES TAPES SPRING, 2001
GOOD FEELS GOOD & BAD FEELS BAD

G-1/13/01-B — Must worries of yesterday affect today? Maverick "12-Stepper" wants improved health. Suffering "Catholic guilt" over miraculous manifestations. Will low classroom grades affect future Well-being? "Senior citizen's" health, and her annoyed expectations. Inner Being never gives you orders. She fired them from "toxic workplace".

G-1/21/01 — Lift your hands from the hot stove. She was diagnosed as manic-depressive, bipolar. Can we discuss other vibrational physical realities? Earth, as the Nonphysical place of choice. He deliberately looked for their Positive Aspects. Releasing her guilt regarding paternal sexual relationship? A loving closing of the Tallahassee Workshop!

G-1/27/01 — Good feels good and bad feels bad. The meaning of her severely retarded child? Does abortion process snuff out Life Force? There's a bump in her relationship road. Opportunities come before her readiness to act. If needed again, your clutter will reappear. Is she loving caring for dying mother?

G-2/3/01 — If you could rewind and replay it. What is your overall mood about money? Time for a self employment "leap of faith". Love others, as he loves his children? Carnivorous alligators, and resolving other disempowering beliefs? Does daughter embody her grandfather's Inner Being? Husband seems undecided between her and freedom.

G-2/17/01 — Mother's dream of son's accident came true. About the entity formerly known as "Abraham". All American basketball contender recaptures his zone. Is mother supporting, or asserting, child's choices? Wanting to be a conduit for healing. Emotions indicate spread between desire and belief. When another's desires make him feel selfish?

G-2/20/01 — Don't leave home without your Inner Being. At feelings Hub of her Thought Wheel. Brain functions, Alzheimer's, ADHA, Hyperactivity, causes, cures? When fun becomes a habit, becomes addiction? Big Bang, Little Bang and 17 Seconds. Her Inner Being's relationship to her finances? Why does she sabotage peak spiritual experiences?

G-2/24/01 — To throw his fast ball fast enough? They won the Mardi Gras "beads lottery". She's still riding on the "Wheel" of guardedness. At a loss for the right words? She's so happy, and he's so unhappy. Consciousness of Martin Luther King still expanding. Making a difference with high school kids?

G-3/10/01 — Which path should this actor painfully pursue? Does sadness make his happiness happier? Any quick fixes for societies' children? Optimist is in love with a pessimist. Children and animals and medicine that works. Must he really bear this disease forever? The truth about tax avoidance group's seminars?

G-3/17/01 — You ask; Universe yields; let it in! What can he do to feel love? To Focus Wheel a Rampage of Appreciation. What are mother's obligations to divorced children? She's getting lots of everything except time. Isn't home schooling about freedom to choose? Twin's preverbal siblings are having ownership issues.

G-3/20/01 — Is your dish locked on to the satellite? An 80 word synopsis regarding health studies? Do we have an insidious (chauvinistic) tendency? What work should she be doing now? His non conformance to an unhappy society. Good foods, bad foods, blah, blah, blah. Your every desire is beneficial to all.

NEW ABRAHAM-HICKS CENTER

It was our intention to ask Billy Mitchell to come out to the property to take some shots of the new Conference Center Building so that we could use it to give you some indication of how thrilled we are with its progress, and with its potential for bringing a great deal of pleasure to a great many of us who will be participating in the time to come. But, our staff, aware of the camera man, all squeezed in, in front of the shot. So instead we'll tell you a little bit about them.

The other day Esther and I decided to sit down together and, on separate pieces of paper, write out a number of positive aspects of some of the people who are close to us and important to our experience. And since we were at home, our thoughts went immediately to our Abraham-Hicks Publications staff, this group of people that you see in this picture who make this business work so well. One of the first things that each of us wrote was how much fun each of them are and how much fun we have when we are together. And as you can probably see, this picture bears that out. We appreciated them for their good natures, for their love of our clients, for their punctuality, for their varied skills, for their sense of Well-being. It just went on and on.

And we'll have to tell you, we don't know how much it did for our staff, but it left Esther and I on such a high we were floating (and actually giggling) for most of the rest of the day. Doesn't it feel good to have people in your life that you respect so much? Doesn't it feel good to be able to share with others the good that you are receiving in your life? Doesn't it feel good to focus your attention on the positive aspects of all of those who are close to you? I don't know about you, but for us, it really does feel good. And, isn't it nice to have people in your life that are easy to love?

In order to put faces to those you communicate with here in our office, from left to right are Barbara Parsons, Gina Bueno, Jana Harkrider, Tracy Ayers, and Joanalie Edwards.

By the time of our San Antonio Open House in April, much of the building that you see in the background will be completed and it won't be long after that that we will be begin conducting workshops in our new center. Ain't it great!!

ABOUT THE AUTHORS

EXCITED ABOUT THE CLARITY and practicality of the translated word from ABRAHAM, Jerry and Esther Hicks began, in 1986, disclosing their ABRAHAM experience to a handful of close business associates. Then, recognizing the practical results being received by those persons who began plying ABRAHAM with meaningful personal questions regarding their finances, bodily conditions, and relationships...the Hickses made a conscious decision to allow ABRAHAM'S teachings to become available to an ever widening circle of seekers. And that circle continues to expand — even as you read this page.

Esther & Jerry Hicks

Jerry and Esther have now published more than 500 *Abraham-Hicks* books, cassettes and videos, and have been presenting open group interactive workshops in about 50 cities a year to those who gather to participate in this progressive stream of thought.

Although worldwide attention has been given by leading edge thinkers to this *Science of Deliberate Creation* who, in turn, incorporate many of ABRAHAM'S concepts into their books, lectures, sermons, screenplays and scripts, the primary spread of this material has been from person to person — as individuals begin to discover the value of these materials in their practical, personal experience.

ABRAHAM, a group of obviously evolved teachers, speak their broader Non-Physical perspective through the physical apparatus of Esther. *Speaking to our level of comprehension, from their present moment to our now, through a series of loving, allowing, brilliant yet comprehensively simple, recordings in print and in sound — they guide us to a clear connection with our Inner Being — they guide us to self-upliftment from our total self.*

COMMENTS FROM READERS & LISTENERS:

...It's hard to believe that life could be so simple and so joyous... Thank you, so much, for making an already good life even better! (With lots of good feelings) SC — PA

...I've been a "searcher," "seeker," "sharer" since I was a teen. My middle name was purported to be "Why?" The information from Abraham is so down-to-earth, useful, compelling, exciting, sensible, practical, empowering, clear, usable. I'm a marvelous deliberate creator now. Thanks for putting the "fun" back into physical life. JS — AZ

...Am so delighted to be reading your books, listening to your tapes and attending your seminars. I am so happy and getting happier and clearer every day. My life has been leading to this point, and it feels like the icing on the cake. I know everything will just get better, although it's hard to know how. What a powerful gift you've given us — the recognition of our ability to create the life we want, and the tools to carry out the plan. Thank you for sharing. — CA

The Value of Conscious Breathing

Deep breathing is a big part of your Well-being, because with that deep breath, there is activation on a cellular level. In other words, it is the current that carries the vitality to the extremities of the cells. And so, the more you are breathing, the more you are thriving.

Some say it is the way the Spirit moves. We would say it is the way life moves most efficiently through your physical body. And, fortunately, it is something that is not left to your conscious mind. You don't have to prompt yourself to breathe. It happens. But you *can* prompt yourself to breathe more.

We encourage that you deliberately take some air in. And then before you let it out, take some more air in. And then before you let it out, take some more air in. And before you let it out... And you say, "I can't take any more in, because there's no place for it to go." And we say, yes there is, take some more in.

Expand your capacity. Your lungs, like balloons, can be all shriveled up, or expanded fully. As you move on a regular basis, they expand somewhat, but they don't expand fully. As you deliberately breathe deeper, it becomes more natural for them to get fuller — and before you know it, it will be an involuntary thing. You will naturally breathe more deeply.

When you're running or moving your body, you don't have to think about it, your body demands it. But when you are sitting, as in an environment like this Workshop, it's very helpful to deliberately breathe in more, breathe in more, breathe in more, breathe in more. And when you think that you cannot breathe in any more — breathe in more. And then experience the deliciousness of a long, easy, out, out, out, out, out. And then breathe in more, breathe in more, breathe in more.

And as you do this more deliberately, you will begin to do it more involuntarily — and your bodies will thrive. It's even more important than drinking water. It's right up there with life itself.

When concentrating on your breathing, you are not concentrating on other things. And in that absence of resistance, you are also allowing an alignment of Energy. So you get a double whammy with it: You're aligning with Source Energy. You are literally feeding the cells of your body, allowing oxygen to reach the extremities of your cells. Everybody comes alive — and everything works better. Metabolism works better, elimination works better, clarity works better, blood flows better. Thriving comes from this.

> Some say that your breathing is the way the Spirit moves. We agree. Your breathing is the way life moves through your physical body.

(Excerpted from Abraham-Hicks Workshop, G-11/25/00— San Antonio, TX)